SO GREAT
A LOVER

LIAM BROPHY

SO GREAT
A LOVER

FRANCISCAN HERALD PRESS
Publishers of Franciscan Literature
Chicago 9, Illinois

SO GREAT A LOVER·
Library of Congress Catalog Card Number: 60-53101
Copyright 1960 by Franciscan Herald Press
1434 West 51st Street, Chicago, Illinois
Designed by Publication Associates
MADE IN THE UNITED STATES OF AMERICA

NIHIL OBSTAT
Marion A. Habig O.F.M.
Mark Hegener O.F.M.
Censores Librorum

IMPRIMI POTEST
Dominic Limacher O.F.M.
Minister Provincial

IMPRIMATUR
† Albert Cardinal Meyer
Archbishop of Chicago

October 17, 1960

To my wife,

the dear embodiment of love in action

Chapter 1

A MEDITERRANEAN SPRING, FRAG-
rant with pines and the blossoms of fruit trees, lay over the island
of Mallorca. Young Prince James rested on a grassy slope high
up in the hills and surveyed his new kingdom with a gaze that
he hoped embodied the proper mixture of benevolence and
sophistication. Only the day before yesterday he had been a
fourteen-year-old schoolboy, shouting and racing through the
echoing halls of the Almudaina Palace. Today—and James felt
his breath catch in his throat at the thought—he was a ruler.

It was difficult to get used to. There were many questions the
boy would have liked to ask his companion, a dark-haired man
of twenty-three who lounged on the grass beside him. Raymond
Lull had been the Prince's confidant, and lately tutor, for as long
as the boy could remember. Surely he would not laugh at the
strange mood in which James now found himself.

And yet the boy hesitated. He was now a ruler—and Raymond
was no longer his teacher but his senechal. Was it not beneath
the dignity of a ruler to ask naive questions of those beneath
him? Everything seemed so different now. Even his old friend
Raymond had a new tone to his voice when, on the ride up to

the hills, he had admonished the young Prince to sit tall in his saddle. The rebuke was surely a familiar one — yet it had sounded different this morning. Then, all at once, James knew what it was. On other days, Raymond had addressed a boy. This morning, he had spoken to a ruler, and a ruler must be a man. Raymond had spoken to him as to a fellow adult.

James sighed, and a faint smile crossed his lips. He was a man, now governor and some day to be king of this beautiful island of vine terraces and olive groves, of jagged cliffs above the azure sea, and misty valleys, full of almond trees. His domain was small compared with the vast, harsh lands of Spain that would be the heritage of his haughty elder brother, Peter; but no land on earth could compare with Mallorca.

"I see you are thoughtful, my Jaime," his companion remarked.

"Only thinking of how I prefer our dear Mallorca to Aragon, Raymond."

"You rule the Fortunate Isles—and here we sit on the Isle of Love itself!"

James assumed an urbane expression. If he was a man, he would speak as a man. "Indeed, you may well call it the Isle of Love, Raymond. I've heard rumors that you have made love to every girl on the island except Maria, old Juan the potter's daughter—and she has a bad temper and crossed eyes."

His friend laughed. But was not the gaiety a bit forced? "My Jaime has too much good sense to believe all that reaches his ears from the tongue-clackers of the court."

"I envy you your good fortune with the ladies, Raymond. Perhaps I will allow you to tutor me in this one last thing."

Raymond Lull sat upright and clasped his knees. His face was clouded. "My good fortune? You envy me, my Prince?"

"I—I do," the boy said hesitantly. "I did not mention it be-

8

fore, because you yourself never saw fit to discuss it with me. But I have heard tales of your search for perfect beauty and love—"

"And have you also heard that I have never succeeded in my quest? Oh, Jaime, Jaime, do not envy a man such as me. To you, the search for ideal love seems romantic and chivalrous. But I know that it brings only torment to the pursuer, seeking the treasure in one lovely face after another. The hungry heart passes from woman to woman, thinking: Here is fulfilment! Here is ecstasy and the sum of all joys! But again and again our straining arms fold about nothing but emptiness. The ideal eludes us once more, calls us to take up our search yet another time."

He broke off and laid his hand gently on the young Prince's shoulder. "Why should I burden you with my dark dreams, Jaime? Forgive me, my boy. Forgive the poor tutor who cannot school his own unruly heart."

"I will not speak of it if it saddens you, my dear friend." James changed the subject with the facility of the young. "My own dreams are quite different. Often when I look across our Mediterranean there, to the south, I dream of conquering all North Africa for Spain. Here I am, in the year of God's grace 1256, with it scarcely 30 years since my father wrested these islands from the Moors. I dream that when I am a bit older, I shall lead my victorious army into Morocco itself and force the conquered infidels to bow before the standard of the True Cross."

"Thus speaks the son of the conqueror," said Raymond fondly. "And who knows, but you may succeed where the good King Louis failed. What a pity he was taken captive after the defeat of Mansura. But for this, the crusade might have had a more blessed ending. And yet, Jaime, I sometimes doubt that

9

the fanatical followers of the Prophet will ever be truly converted by the sword."

"The desecrators and destroyers of the Holy Land *must* be put down by the strength of armies," declared the Prince. "How else could we subdue them?"

"To subdue is one goal. To convert is quite a different one. We cannot touch the souls of men by means of hate and fury."

The Prince smiled loftily. "You have advised me well in the technique of government, Raymond. But there are other duties which we princes may assume. We may conquer in God's name."

From the valley below came the sound of the evening Angelus bell, resounding among the hills to surround them with its throbbing pulse. The Prince pointed to the distant church. "There, before my father's time, stood a mosque. Where our Lady's bell rings now, sunrises and sunsets of centuries have heard the muezzin call the infidels to prayer. The change was wrought by the might of my father's sword. How else could a king have accomplished this?"

"You are wise indeed, Jaime," said Raymond, bowing his head slightly. "There was no other way—for a king."

As they rode homeward at the head of a small retinue, the light drained away almost magically from the valleys, leaving only the sea-cliffs and the lustrous waters themselves still lit by the sun. The air grew cooler. In the town of Palma, the capital of James's small kingdom, people sat at wide-flung lattices or leaned on quaint wrought-iron balustrades to enjoy the rich mingling of perfumes that arose at dusk.

The chattering courtiers grew silent. The young Prince was lost in his own contemplations, and the seneschal, Raymond Lull, found his thoughts drifting into the past. He rode again, not by the side of Prince James, but as a page in the train of

King James the Conqueror. They had traveled to Valencia for the rout of the Moors; to Perpignan, where he had won the Conqueror's interest by means of a felicitously composed ballad, and had been made a squire; to Montpellier, Barcelona, and Saragossa; to Huesca, in a hurried winter journey, to where the gentle Queen Violante lay dying.

The evening's chill recalled to Raymond how he had held the death-cold hand of the Queen; he beheld once more her dim eyes, trying to search his thirteen-year-old face as she bequeathed to his care her tiny youngest son, James. He had not betrayed her trust. As playmate and then as teacher he had fulfilled the promise made to the dying woman in Huesca. And yesterday Raymond had stood at the boy's right hand as he received the homage of his Mallorquin subjects. He would rule well. . . .

The memories faded, for already they were entering beneath the rounded arch of the Arab gate, leading to the Calle del Almudaina and the palace walls.

Raymond's parents, members of a noble Catalonian family, had received their Mallorcan lands as a reward for assisting King James in his conquests. It was a source of pride to them that their son had been appointed Grand Seneschal; but their pride was darkened by sorrow at his dissolute life. Perhaps his revels were to be attributed to his youth and high spirits; it was their hope that marriage would put an end to the gossip that stained his name. They confided these hopes to the Prince, young as he was, and begged him to arrange a marriage for Raymond's own good. The Prince listened gravely, and promised to do what he could.

Toward the end of the summer, Prince James left for the Court at Montpellier, with Raymond a member of the entourage. When the royal party returned in the spring of 1257, there was an unusually large crowd gathered at the quayside to meet the ships. Rumors had been circulating since January that Raymond had married at last, and the people of Palma were anxious for many reasons to know on whom his—or the Prince's— choice had fallen.

When the royal barge pulled alongside the quay and the gangway was let down, the crowd surged forward to catch a glimpse of the pale, quiet woman on the arm of Don Raymond. Her name, they knew, was Doña Blanca Picany.

"She's fair enough," remarked a portly merchant, "but I hear her wealth is a deal fairer."

"You've given ear to the wrong rumor, my friend," said a one-eyed man who wore the garb of a sea captain. "It is well known in the ports of Spain that the gentle Doña Blanca comes of a noble but impoverished family. They say the Conqueror himself settled a dowry on her, probably at our Prince's request, to put an end to Don Raymond's philandering."

A buxom beauty whose apron was stained with fish scales stood on tiptoe to view the disembarking royal party. "Don Raymond give up his pleasures for *her* sake?" She gave a saucy laugh. "One might as well ask a bee to sip honey from one flower—and a colorless one at that. Would you be content to stay faithful to a pale anemone when you could have a garden of roses?"

"I? I?" demanded the man of the sea. "I demand not even roses—not so long as there are tempting little mermaids like you to chaff with me in every port I visit!"

The crowd moved along, following the colorful procession as gaily caparisoned horses were led up and the noblemen assisted the ladies to mount.

"Poor little bride," murmured old Camila the melon seller.

"She looks too sweet and modest. Such a child. May our holy St. Eulalia give her joy."

"She will need the assistance of the whole saintly calendar to tame the lusty Don Raymond," the sea captain prophesied.

The new household of Raymond Lull and his lady appeared serene for several months. The Prince installed Doña Blanca in her place of honor in the Mallorquin court, and the ladies vied with one another to provide feasts and entertainments that would prove to her that Mallorca was far from being a provincial outpost of King James's realm.

Raymond, of course, was often away on official business. But gradually his absences became more frequent and lasted longer. He was discreet—but there were always tale-bearers willing to fill the ears of the young wife with hints and insinuations.

The grayness of winter was brightened for Blanca by the birth of a baby boy; and for a while again Raymond was at her side, possessive and proud. He lavished love on the infant Dominic, and when a daughter, Magdalena, was born the following year, Raymond swore that no man in the world could be so happy as he. He composed songs and made up games for his children and their mother, and Blanca knew the happiest years of her life.

And then the melancholy restlessness returned. Blanca had by now begun to recognize in her husband the strange humors and quicksilver changes in temperament that seemed to go hand in hand with his brilliance and witty charm. His dark moods were usually short. The coming of the children had for a time banished them completely, but now a vast turmoil once more held his soul in thrall. On the surface, Raymond was ever the chivalrous cavalier, courteous and solicitous of her material welfare. Within, he was a man on fire; and gossips were eager to apprise Doña Blanca of the lengths to which his passion had driven him.

13

Blanca resolved to center her life in the children, and let the scandals of her husband's affairs glance off her little world like arrows off castle walls. She was almost relieved when he announced that he was undertaking a long journey, traveling to Montpellier to witness the formal profession of allegiance of the nobles to Prince Peter, brother of James of Mallorca. He would then go on to Barcelona for the announcement of the engagement of the princes' sister, Elizabeth, to Philip, son of the saintly Louis of France.

Rumors flew back to Mallorca like ugly black birds, invariably homing their way to Blanca's heart in spite of her efforts to shut them out. But when Raymond returned, she did not reproach him. Still shackled by his unquenchable lust, despising himself but too proud to admit his guilt, he simply avoided meeting her and retired to his own apartments.

Raymond's behavior in the weeks that followed was a public scandal. He boasted that there was no woman born who could resist him once he laid siege to her heart. Finally, in the summer of 1260, the storm broke. Doña Blanca poured out the ultimate sordid episode in a letter to her sister in Barcelona:

Inez, my dearest sister,

Many times I have begun to write to you these past weeks, only to put aside pen and paper in the hope that the blessed Savior would be mindful of my tears and prayers so that the tidings I send to you would be those of joy. Alas, my supplications receive no answer, and I can endure no more. The thought that my innocent darlings should suffer because of the demon lust that consumes my lord Raymond's heart has driven me almost to madness.

God alone knows what devil seized my lord on this Sunday evening, that he should gallop his horse in mad pursuit of his base passion into the very house of God! Worse sacrilege was prevented because the congregation at Compline pressed about him and forced him outside the church. But he was quite beside himself and followed this woman to her house — no wanton light-of-love, either, but a lovely and pious woman, Ambrosia di Castello, the happy wife of a Genoese merchant but lately settled here. It seems he has pestered her with his vile attentions, singing early and late beneath her window and hanging about her door like a cur waiting for the table-scraps.

The Doña Ambrosia had my wretched husband admitted and brought to her bower, where she had previously secreted two female attendants behind the arras. Thinking they were alone at last, my lord poured forth his foolish speech of adulation; whereupon she said: "Gaze then upon the body that has driven you to profane God's house and place your own soul within reach of the fires of hell!" Whereupon she drew aside the lace at the front of her dress and showed him her breast all rotted and eaten away by cancer.

Poor courageous soul! Yet I would most willingly exchange with her this moment. She suffers less than I, who have this sorrow tearing out my heart.

Raymond staggered out of the house to lose himself in the darkness. May God pity him and deliver him from the devil that enslaves him! I am a fool, Inez, for I listen for his step upon the stair, and I think if he were to come now, as often before, and lay his repentant head on my knee like a small, bold boy, everything would be blotted out for me but my love. . . .

But he does not come. And my son and daughter shall not stay here to suffer the jibes and sneers of loiterers and low-born wastrels. So I shall set sail for our estate at Barcelona with all speed. Dear Inez, please meet me there with your good lord Carlos. But do not sadden our parents' hearts with my sorrow.

Until we meet, my sister, God be with you!

In the days after Doña Blanca and the children had gone, Raymond wandered about the empty villa, haunted by the memory of that hideous Sunday night. Servants fled at his approach as from a maniac. There was no rest during the day, and night brought only dreams of decay and rottenness that rose up between him and his quest for the ideal love.

The ideal love! But it was still real, he told himself; love was still real, still true, still beautiful and undying. If he could only find it. . . .

He turned again to the only love his dissolute heart knew—the red lips and soft caressing arms. He tuned his lute again and vowed to compose ballads such as had never been dreamed of. He would enshrine love in his songs, deathless and lovely, for later ages and other lovers. In the torrid air of a summer evening, he sat in his shaded gallery looking out over the garden toward the sea. He hummed and wrote by turns, tapping out the rhythm on the table.

As he struggled for the right turn of phrase, he lifted his head from time to time. Suddenly, on the white plastered wall, there appeared to him a Face—the Savior, transfixed with agony.

Raymond sat frozen with fear. Then, in a panic of terror, he leaped up and rushed to his room, flinging himself on his bed and burying his head to shut out the awful persistence of that sorrowful gaze.

The servants who had seen him rush by paid little heed, for they were accustomed to their master's wild ways. What did surprise them was the sound of sobbing that came from beyond the closed door. Gradually this died away and silence settled over the palace.

When he awoke next morning, it was easy to convince himself that the vision had resulted from a touch of sun—or overwrought nerves brought on by the fervency of his artistic mood. He would leave his song until he had steadied himself. No doubt the mood would pass away soon.

But Raymond could not long stifle his urge to write. He set

out his papers again, this time in the rose-bower beside the pool, with somber cypresses standing guard beyond. He began to hum the tune again—a little lamely at first, but gradually losing himself in the work of creation.

It happened again. There, clear and in full sunlight against the cypresses, the Figure of the Crucified hung before him. This time, Raymond fled to the cellars of the villa, and the servants whispered that the mad Don Raymond was roaring and weeping among the wine casks.

Raymond had been proud of his inflexible and masterful will. "Neither blows, nor punishments, nor pleasures, nor caresses, nor wiles of any man avail either to mould my will or to check it," he had said of himself. But now it was no man who opposed him, but God. In vain did the Grand Seneschal seek to immerse himself once more in the gaiety of the court. Christ appeared a third time, a fourth time, a fifth time.

All through the night of his fifth vision, Raymond was in agony. He knew now who it was who sought him, who had conquered him. His old life was in ashes, his old ideal of human love lay dead with a new, eternal Love arisen in its place. By daybreak he had decided that God wanted him to turn completely from the world and give himself entirely to the divine service.

With characteristic directness, he went straight to the church and laid his stupendous burden of sin before a priest. As God's pardon was pronounced over him, his new life began.

But what kind of a life was it to be?

Chapter 2

THE NEWS OF RAYMOND'S APPAR-
ent conversion from a life of scandal spread much more slowly
than the word of his escapades had, and it was a general con-
sensus that the change in his behavior was probably only a temporary one. Nevertheless, the Grand Seneschal stayed aloof
from his former companions throughout the following winter
and spring. To those who inquired after him, he replied: "My
time is taken up with the last great Love of my heart."

Maytime came, and soft winds blew the petals of the almond
blossoms like pink snow through the valley of Valldemosa. The
intuitive mind of Raymond was quick to see the symbolism: his
own springtime was spent, its blossoms wantonly scattered.
Those wasted years must be redeemed while there was still time.

Raymond had become accustomed to take long walks during
his strange new moods of exaltation, often bursting into spon-
taneous hymns of his own composition, or debating with himself
on what course his life should take.

"I have discovered the greatest Love!" he would declaim to
the gnarled olive trees. "But my lord Jesus requires that I return
love for love—and how am I to best do this? It is not enough to

sigh in rapture—to sing, to glory in God's goodness to me. I am not a songbird, but a man! A man must work for his love, even die for it. . . . Shall I die, then, Lord? I fear I have neither strength nor grace to die simply for love of you, as some of the blessed saints have done. Perhaps I could die as a martyr! Ah, there is a challenge to tempt the lover—'Greater love than this no man has, than he should lay down his life for his friend.' Lord, could I be worthy of such a death as this?"

Raymond was so absorbed that he did not notice that a Franciscan friar had come down the narrow road leading through the olive grove and now stood aside to permit him to pass by.

"*Perdoneme,* Don Raymond," said the friar, recognizing the soliloquizer. "I did not mean to intrude upon your—"

"My one-sided conversation?" Raymond smiled. "In truth, it must have sounded strange to you, Fray Angelo. But do not be in a hurry to pass me by. I have really been longing for someone to talk to—to discuss the state of my soul. No one seems more suitable than a follower of the humble and courteous Francis of Asissi."

"I would be honored, your excellency," said the friar. He was somewhat at a loss. Was this not the notorious Raymond Lull, said by some to be mad? The Franciscan knew his duty lay in charity, but he resolved to have recourse to prudence, too.

Raymond resumed his pacing. "You will be startled to know that the Crucified has appeared to one as unworthy as me—even as he appeared to your beloved Francis. Five times in all my Beloved came to me, until my hard and sinful heart was finally moved. I am consumed with loathing for my scandalous life, and I have made up my mind to follow Christ."

Fray Angelo was so taken aback at this extraordinary speech that he could only murmur, "Most remarkable! Most remarkable, indeed!

"Do you remember how our beloved Lord gave Francis his special vocation to go and build his Church which had fallen into ruin?"

"Indeed, Don Raymond, 40 years have passed since our holy founder was taken to heaven, and yet our Order strives to carry out his work."

"Yes, yes," said Raymond impatiently. "And one of the ways that Francis undertook this work was to go himself and send his followers to convert the Saracens and other infidels."

"That is true."

Raymond's dark eyes flashed. "I feel this call, too, Fray Angelo! I am becoming more and more convinced that it is God's will for *me* to undertake a new type of crusade."

The friar could scarcely conceal his alarm. "Our father Francis was a bringer of peace—but the crusaders have laid too much stress on the sword. For this reason the Lord has allowed their undertaking to come to naught."

"You misunderstand, Fray Angelo. I would inaugurate a crusade of quite another kind. I would have men skilled in the doctrines of our Faith, men of God speaking the language of the infidel with perfect fluency. How can we convert by means of an interpreter? We cannot! But missionaries who speak the language of the Saracens could touch the hearts of the simple people as well as the learned. Think of it! Hosts of holy men pouring into Africa and the Holy Places—preaching and baptizing as they go!"

"A splendid dream. A truly Franciscan dream," said Fray Angelo, caught up in spite of himself by Raymond's enthusiasm.

"And I have yet another Franciscan dream, Fray Angelo, more daring than the last. It is that I may some day lay down my life for Christ and the Gospel. You of course recall how much Francis longed and prayed for just that."

21

"A glorious privilege, your excellency. And who but God knows what may be?" They paused at a fork in the road. "But here I must leave you. Be assured of my prayers, Don Raymond, and Godspeed."

The dark gray habit was soon lost among the silver-gray of the olive leaves, and Raymond was left alone again with his surging thoughts. He felt convinced that he could convert the unbelievers by showing them where they were wrong and breaking down their prejudices and ignorance. But first, he would have to win their friendship. Love was better than logic at the beginning—as any troubador knew full well.

As majordomo of the royal house he was used to ordering and getting things into shape, as well as conducting inventories from time to time. He took stock of himself now. Granted he had some skill in writing verses. That would be of little use now. What he needed was a proficiency in Latin and Arabic. He was just 30 years of age now and his memory was not as good as it used to be. A mountain of hard study lay before him, but he was determined to scale it for the sake of Christ.

His spirits revived as he added certain points in his favor. He had been on intimate terms with kings and princes, and so he could approach them for help. James the Conqueror had always been keenly interested in the conversion of the Jews and Moslems, and Raymond knew he could depend on him to further his plans.

He was also certain to have the cooperation of young Prince James, and even the sullen-tempered Peter could be forced to help. Raymond's friends in high places could not refuse him now that he was ambassador to the King of Kings.

The year wore on. Raymond continued his solitary musings, which took him one day to a small wood near Raxa on the coast. Pausing to look through the trees, he saw the Mediterranean stretching before him like a vast level plain, reaching all the way to Africa. He felt sure his greatest challenge lay there.

Suddenly there was a sound behind him. *"Siento mucho molestarle, Señor,"* said the slightly hostile voice of a swarthy *campesino.* He tied his mule to a nearby tree and sat down under it. Studying the newcomer, Raymond decided that he must be one of the Moors to whom the island had formerly belonged. James the Conqueror had allowed a number of them to remain as slaves to the Christians. They were naturally resentful of the usurpers, and the man's voice betrayed poorly concealed hate.

Raymond decided to ignore the tone. Here was his first challenge in the new life he had chosen. Could he get behind this man's thoughts?

"You are not disturbing me, my friend," the Grand Seneschal said genially. "I was simply resting here, watching the sea, wondering what is going on in Africa just now."

The Moor rose to the bait. "How could things go but ill for the invaders, Señor! Your crusades will come to nothing! Does not your own Holy Book say that they who take the sword will perish by the sword? Yet these Christian soldiers go forth preaching the God of love and kill the Moslems in their own lands. Can one be surprised that Allah does not bring them victory?"

The Moor was abruptly silent. Perhaps he felt that he had already said too much.

Raymond searched his soul for a reply, but none would come. What could he say to this man? Within himself, he also felt that the crusades had accomplished little. True, Acre and Tripoli were in Christian hands at the moment; but the Holy Sepulchre and the Holy Land itself were still firmly held by the Saracens. Despite the blessings of popes and prelates, despite the fervor and bravery of the knights, God had not seen fit to crown the crusades with success. The Moor's bitter words seemed to be true—and yet there must be another answer to the problem!

"My friend," Raymond said, "it may be that you are right about this clashing of armies and shedding of blood. Nonetheless, all Christians do not feel hatred toward the children of Islam. It may be that some time in the future a new army will descend into the lands of your people—a peaceful army whose only weapons are love and learning. They would speak your language and engage in debates with your wise men. Instead of attempting to conquer by the sword, the new army would win over your people through teaching them about our God and his love for all men."

The Moor did not speak, but only sat regarding Raymond with dark, mistrustful eyes.

"I bid you *adios,*" Raymond said. And with a courteous nod, he began to descend to the town. The brief incident had showed him that he must learn the art of debate, study the viewpoint of his opponents, familiarize himself thoroughly with their history and temperament. The new army would, above all, have to fortify itself by means of prayer and penance; only seasoned warriors of the spirit would be able to withstand the assaults of the unbelievers.

Raymond's life during this period seemed to him somewhat like the topography of Mallorca itself. There were many peaks and vantage points, some exotically fair like Miramar, others austere like Randa. Between these heights there were deep valleys and woodlands that could be jasmine-scented and delightful —or bleak and depressing wastelands.

His withdrawal from the gay life he had formerly known became complete. Summer merged into fall, one of the most beau-

tiful seasons of the island. Dahlias, cosmos, marigolds and car-
nations brightened the gardens of Palma. Aloes, with brown
fleshy leaves, starred the dry fields with their yellow flowers.
Hanging clematis and geraniums made cascades of color over
the ancient walls. Raymond was a man who used to notice such
things and glory in them; but now he was lost in other thoughts.

One morning in October, he saw a crowd larger than usual
making its way to the newly constructed church of San Francisco
in Palma, where workmen were still carving pillars for the cloisters at the rear. He suddenly remembered that this was the feast
of the saint of Assisi, the little Poor Man who had partaken so
eagerly of the love of Christ that he had been imprinted with
Christ's own wounds.

Raymond stepped into the church, a strange mood wrapped
about him. He felt as if he were on the threshold of a great dis-
covery. The bishop sang Mass this morning, and when he ascended the pulpit for the sermon, Raymond listened to his words
with an attention that was as taut as the strings of a lute.

The bishop spoke of St. Francis as a man sent from God to
rekindle the love of the Gospels in a world that had grown cold
and indifferent. The key to the saint's success, said the bishop,
lay in the completeness of his surrender and self-sacrifice. He
had shed his very clothes as a sign of his complete fidelity to *la
Dona Poverta*; and as he did so, great joy and freedom had possessed him with the boundless energy of a great love.

Raymond felt that the words of the bishop were directed to
him alone, that the message was flowing to his heart as straight
as the sunbeams that burned through the windows of the
crowded church. He had heard much of the Poor Man of Assisi,
who had been a troubador of merit even as Raymond himself.
And the Beloved had spoken to Francis until he became a lamp
of love, the happiest man on earth with only one sorrow—that

Love was not loved enough.

Raymond saw himself a foul sinner compared with the seraphic Francis. Still, if he dared as much, could Heaven fail to assist him? He would choose as his bride *la Dona Valor*—Lady Bravery.

The new mood which now seized Raymond Lull amazed and scandalized his former companions even more than had his life of sin. He decided that he must give up his possessions and break completely with his past. He set aside enough of his property to support his wife and children, and the rest was sold and the proceeds distributed to the poor of Palma. Then he spoke of going on a long pilgrimage. He would be away, he told the Prince, for an indefinite period.

This was worse than any *grande pasion!* One day an old associate named Rodrigo came to remonstrate with him.

"You cannot imagine, my dear Raymond, how dull the night-life in Palma has become without your wit and song. Life becomes as flat as peasant wine when you are seized by one of these odd humors. They cannot be good for your health, my friend! You are a man of vigor, of fire—not a monk! Do not let this unnatural fever bring you to disaster."

"There will be no disaster, Don Rodrigo," said Raymond dryly. "My health is excellent, and I have no doubt that you and the other lovers of gaiety will soon find another master of ceremonies."

"But none like you, old friend," said Rodrigo with a wag of his beard. "And what is this nonsense about a pilgrimage? We have seen you make many a pilgrimage to the shrines of Venus, but this is something we can understand! What will the court be without you? And how will the young Prince manage?"

"He is wise beyond his years, and I have made arrangements for his counsel. The time has come for me to take up other work, *amigo,* and I will not be dissuaded from it."

"Alas, but have it your own way. You will leave lonely hearts behind you. I recall how you said it was impossible to find happiness with women—but for one such as you, it is also impossible to find happiness without them."

Raymond became irritated by the banter of this man, who with his caustic tongue and jeweled, useless hands seemed to symbolize the world's folly. It would do no good to open his heart to this old cynic, or tell him of the great things his Beloved had wrought in him. Yet even for such as Don Rodrigo there must be charity.

"Tell my old friends that I am off to revisit old places, to try a new way of life, to get away from the complications and distractions that have brought me no happiness. Tell them what you have planned to say anyway—that I am a little mad."

Once more, Raymond watched the Isle of Love from beneath the swelling sails of a ship, fading into the haze that blurred the horizon. But on his other journeys he had gone as the royal seneschal, with laughing comrades to accompany him and the prospects of adventure and diversions ahead of him. This time, he was alone, a poor pilgrim, with only hardship and penance to look forward to. Yet, he had never known the feeling of peace that now rested upon him. He stood at the rail of the ship, apart from the other passengers, and only smiled when a sharp feminine voice remarked that he was probably chasing after some new love. She was right. And he would follow this Love until the very end of his days.

For nearly two years, the pilgrim of love passed from one great shrine to another—Montserrat, Rocamadour, St. James at Compostela—expiating his long years of sin. He went to Rome to pray at the Tomb of St. Peter, and even visited the Holy Land, toward which he was often to look back with longing and desire.

Sometimes a great surge of sorrow and love would mount in his heart when he thought of Blanca and the children. How shamefully he had treated them and how he longed now to gather them to his heart and to atone for all of his faithlessness! But he would remind himself that he had now set aside his own will to do the will of his Beloved, and the thought gave him comfort and strength in his human loneliness.

Finally, he found his way to Barcelona in Spain, where he decided to seek the advice of the great Dominican, Raymund of Peñafort. It was said that the saintly Fray Ramon had even counseled and advised the great Thomas Aquinas, and Raymond had already met the Dominican, who had been the Conqueror's confessor and adviser.

Fray Ramon had predicted that great things were in store for the passionate young seneschal, and so he was not greatly surprised to see him a changed man, penitent and fervent before him.

Raymond described his conversion and pilgrimage, and told how he planned now to go to Paris to study.

"Ah," said the old friar. "You wish to complete your education?"

"Ah, no, Padre. I am just beginning."

"A beginner in Paris? My son, you are beginning your climb at the top of the ladder. A little schoolroom in Palma will serve you better than the lecture halls of the university. Now wherefore, may I ask, this thirst for learning?"

Raymond flushed and lowered his head. "You will think it strange, knowing the life I have led. But now that I have changed, I see that it is God's plan for me to win the souls of the Saracens—to succeed where the crusades have failed. I wish to capture the minds of the infidels, to convince them of the truths of our Faith. But first I must study theology and then I will study their language. In God's time I will set up schools everywhere for the study of theology and Arabic, and send legions of learned men to Africa to gather in harvests of souls."

The old Dominican smiled kindly at the young man's enthusiasm. He had less education than a postulant, yet he planned to preach the Gospel in Arabic and found schools! But Raymund of Peñafort saw in his young namesake immense reserves of mental and spiritual energy. It was possible. . . .

"Those are splendid ambitions, my son, and may God strengthen and inspire you. The idea of colleges for oriental languages has often engaged my attention. I have, in fact, founded two—one at Murcia, the other in Tunis. A third is being set up here in Barcelona. But you must realize that a great deal of work lies ahead of you before your dreams will be realized."

"I understand that, *caro Padre,* and that is why I want to begin right away."

"Raymond, Raymond, how I envy you your youth, that perceives not the steepness of the mountain but only the glory of the summit! With perseverance, you will succeed. Now then. You ask my advice on how best to proceed. I have counsel for you, but it will not be easy to follow."

"I will obey you, Fray Ramon. Only tell me what I must do."

"Listen, my son. You must return to your court duties and assume once more the obligations of a husband and parent. At your house in Palma, you must live a life of virtue that will atone for the scandal of your past. At the same time, I will find a tutor for you, and I will permit you to use the books of our convent library. You have years of work ahead of you before you become a worthy messenger of the Gospel—and until you are ready, you must provide for yourself and for your family by doing the secular work for which you have been trained."

"I thought I did the right thing by giving up everything for Christ," Raymond said confusedly.

"Christ does not permit us to give up our *duties* for his sake, my son. You will serve God in God's good time. Go now and prepare for this work."

And so Raymond and his family returned to Palma, and the Prince welcomed his old friend with joy. The court livery seemed a tawdry sham to Raymond, so he had a habit made for himself of the coarsest cloth and wore it everywhere. The reappearance of the once elegant seneschal in this fantastic garb gave the court wits a rare source of amusement, but Raymond found that their jests were easier to bear than he had feared. A sort of divine indifference to the things of the world now shielded him.

To Blanca, who had reluctantly agreed to return to Palma, her husband remained an enigma. He took little interest in administering the lands which he had deeded to her and the children, and scarcely seemed to know what was going on around him. He always treated her with courtesy, deferring to her wishes in all matters that she succeeded in bringing to his attention; but if she ceased to prod and admonish him he was invariably reengulfed in the studies that now seemed to take all his time.

Blanca finally gave up urging him to assume the life of a courtier and landowner. She left him in peace with his books and saw him only from time to time.

During the next nine years, Raymond applied himself with unwavering application to the laying of the foundations of culture. He concentrated especially on the study of Arabic, taught him by a Moorish slave. Raymond grew to have a deep regard for this man, and cherished the hope that some day he would succeed in breaking through the crust of prejudice that walled in the Moslem's soul.

But Raymond did not yet understand the fanatic strength that lay within the hearts of the Mohammedans. One day when the seneschal was absent from home, the slave casually blasphemed the name of Jesus. When this was reported to Raymond, he flogged the man with his own hand. "It is in this name that I will conquer all such as you." Raymond thundered to the cowering slave. "Using this language you have taught me, I will never rest until every Saracen knee bends in reverence at the Name of Jesus!"

The slave's mind was simple. He had not understood why his master wished to learn his tongue; but now that he understood, his heart was filled with fury. He had betrayed his faith by tutoring Raymond.

Knowing nothing of what passed through the Moor's mind, Raymond forgot the incident. But the slave bided his time until one quiet evening when his master sat engrossed in study. With a hoarse cry, the Moor flung himself upon Raymond, stabbing him with a knife stolen from the kitchen. Though badly wounded, Raymond managed to hold the slave until other members of the household rushed to his assistance.

Instant death was the usual punishment for such a crime. But Raymond, thinking of the man's long years of help, was reluctant to send a soul before God if there was a chance of saving it. He postponed his decision for a few days, retreating to the Cistercian monastery of Nuestra Doña de la Real. When he returned home, he found that the decision had been taken out of his hands: the despairing Moor had untied the cord which bound him and hanged himself with it.

Chapter 3

RAYMOND'S MIND, WHICH HAD LAIN fallow for 30 years, now opened to receive the knowledge of the medieval world. From his huge collection of writings, it is clear that nothing he learned was ever lost. Few men have written so much on so many topics. Everything that he heard and saw entered his prodigious memory to be stored there, perfectly preserved, until he needed to recall it. It is abundantly clear in the first book he ever wrote, the great *Book of Contemplation*. This was originally composed in Arabic during his nine-year study of the language, and then translated by him into a million-word Catalan version.

The masterpiece is just what every good novel is supposed to be—a pocket theater. It gives an amazingly vivid and detailed description of the life of the Middle Ages, and is actually very closely related to a novel. It is also an autobiography, since it gives snatches of Raymond's past life, very thinly disguised. Yet another remarkable quality of this vast book is the author's ability to keep several themes revolving around each other in perfect harmony. He carried his troubador's art into literature with consummate skill.

Humor, pathos, satire and a deep compassion for humanity gleam through this book. Tell-tale traits of important personages are brought forth with the art of a caricaturist. Two types in particular are described with fondness—friars and sailors. Lull already showed the Franciscan bent of his mind, for while he describes the elaborate banquets and the rich attire of the wealthy classes of the day, he points out that the good things of life are not to be despised, nor is judgment to be passed on the wearers of gay clothes or the members of the "smart set." They may be camouflaging an interior sanctity.

Tolerance is a virtue that Raymond Lull possessed in abundance. This, too, was a Franciscan trait. His enemies whispered that he went too far in his efforts to see the other person's point of view, but he did so in order to bring souls back with him.

In his studies, he found that there were surprisingly few doctrinal obstacles to the conversion of the Jews and the Mohammedans. The principal ones were the doctrine of the Trinity, the Divinity of Christ, and the virgin birth. The basic flaw was that these unbelievers tried to put a limit to God's omnipotence, and in so doing, by attempting to honor God they ended in dishonoring him.

In many ways Raymond found the Moslems nearer the Christian point of view than the Jews, as, for instance, in their attitude toward our Lady. The Moslems agreed that Christ was conceived by the Holy Spirit; but they said that he was no more than a great prophet. They conceded that our Lady was a virgin before and after the birth of Christ. The Jews, on the other hand, generally scorned the Virgin Mary, denying that her Son was conceived by the Holy Spirit, saying that he was a fallible sinner like any other man.

Lull's studies seemed to have led him to an early belief in the Immaculate Conception, even though scholars dispute his right to the title of First Defender of this doctrine. It is clear from his writings, however, that he considered our Lady to have been born without sin. He used the argument frequently employed by the Franciscans: before a house is actually built, its habitation is foreseen. In the same way, the Redemption was part of God's plan before it was achieved. In his divine foreknowledge, God made everything ready for the coming of his Son—and part of that preparation was Mary's sinlessness.

On a day in the year 1269, Raymond's studies were interrupted by a great tumult that invaded his house.

"Wherefore this prolonged commotion?" he asked his old servingman, Marco. "I fear I must put study away this morning, there is so much noise and excitement in the air."

"You would have heard the news, master, if you had not been so lost in your work. There are comings and goings of great importance. Our Mallorca has mustered the biggest company of crusaders in her history. They are gathering now, and soon they will be on their way to join the saintly King Louis of France."

Raymond put his parchments aside and hurried down into the street to join the throng which was following the colorful cavalcade down to the quayside. There the ships awaited the soldiers and their horses, ready to take them to Aiguesmortes. When the ropes were cast off and the sails began to unfurl and take the wind, Raymond found himself cheering as vigorously as any of the other bystanders. And he sighed a little, too, as the huge crosses on the great sails grew smaller on the horizon and dipped out of sight.

As the year 1270 wore on, disturbing news came from the south in little wisps of rumor and counter-rumor. What did appear certain was that the crusaders had wavered in their plans, and had been prevailed upon by Charles of Anjou to take the route through Carthage so that he might settle some old personal scores.

The autumn winds came earlier that year, and gray skies seemed to presage some failure or disaster to the anxious Mallorcans. Fever, so the messengers reported, had killed more crusaders than had Saracen swords. It did not spare the soldier-king, Louis himself. Then the shattering news came that Louis had died of the fever in August, and that his dispirited army had disintegrated. The high hopes of a few months before came crashing down.

The tidings of defeat touched Raymond's heart like a personal tragedy. He longed most ardently to discuss the turn of events with someone, and when he received news that the Dominican, Raymund of Peñafort, had arrived in Palma, he hastened to meet him.

Their meeting was tinged with sorrow. The old man said, "It is just as we surmised, my son. God does not want a show of physical force, but rather he asks us to conquer the Moslem world through love. If I remember, we were of one mind in this matter."

"The more I have seen and studied, the more I am convinced that a crusade of a different sort is needed to win back the Holy Places. Now that the blessed King Louis has failed, I fear it will be most difficult to raise up a new army."

The Dominican sighed. "This is true. But let us speak of your progress, Raymond. I have been told how you persevere in your studies. Allow me to congratulate you from my heart on your steadfastness. I knew that you would have to pass through the valley of humiliation first, and I prayed for you. And now that you have seen of what little worth the esteem of men is, you can go forth confidently, untrammeled by the opinions of others."

"It was bitter, Fray Ramon, and yet *amor vincit omnia.* Christ was reviled and ridiculed, so why should a wretch such as I complain? Besides, the experience has taught me many things. Those who were friends turned enemies, and those who should be enemies became fast friends."

"I do not quite understand you."

"I went among the Jews and Saracens, and by the gracious permission of the Prince, I was allowed to preach in their synagogues and mosques. I was amazed at their devotion, their love of mercy and justice, and their firm belief in the unity of God."

"True," the friar said. "They possess many admirable qualities. Christians would do well to surpass them in virtue instead of supressing them."

"You have observed yourself, Fray Ramon, that they have become enslaved by custom and the tradition of their fathers. We can understand that. It is not easy for a man to change his way of life, to turn his back on the customs and habits of his people. But if he is to be saved he must do so. The Moslems believe that they will enjoy carnal pleasures in the world to come because they are so fond of them here. They refuse to use their God-given intellects. They use their imagination too much and their reason too little. They seek the truth through their senses. But they must be taught to seek it instead with intellectual and spiritual eyes, using the mirror of understanding."

"Certainly, Raymond, you have given the matter much thought. But sometimes it seems you attach almost too much importance to the understanding. I have been discussing this very point with our learned Thomas of Aquin, who like yourself is writing a monumental work for the refutation and conversion of heretics, and the exaltation of the Faith."

"Perhaps I seem attached to the work of the intellect, Fray Ramon; but when a man discovers what he thinks is a neglected

37

or forgotten aspect of truth, he is perhaps inclined to overstress it."

"Take care, my son, for that way lies heresy."

But Raymond's thoughts surged ahead relentlessly. "True belief must be founded on both intellect and will. These faculties of the soul are united by faith and reason. They are the two feet which carry a man on the way to truth, and they must be used equally and simultaneously."

The two friends passed out of the cool cloisters into the garden of the priory, where the white-robed brothers had fashioned beds of fragrant herbs and modest blossoms. "What will you do now, my son?" asked the old Dominican. "I must tell you that I do not feel you are ready yet to journey over the sea."

"You must tell me why, *caro Padre.*"

"You were fine steel when we met in Barcelona—yet unformed. Now you have been fashioned into a well-balanced blade by your intellectual labors, but still you lack the temper that comes only from the fire of divine Love and the quenching in holy self-abasement. When you have strengthened your will and your love, then your mind can be given its final honing through experience."

"As always, you are right." Raymond bowed to the old man. "I know how this tempering process can be accomplished. Give me your blessing, Fray Raymon, and I will go away at once."

The impetuosity that was characteristic of Raymond led him to cast aside his study and writing. He had been almost immediately convinced that the Dominican was right, that his own mind was too much inclined to mere intellectualism. At times, while writing his book, he felt starved for prayer and union with God. His intellect had been active at the expense of his spirit.

He resolved now to devote himself to his Beloved. He would

find a mountain as St. Francis had found La Verna, where he might speak to God and be uninterrupted by the tumults and tedious affairs of the world. He set out for Mount Randa.

In sharp contrast to the rest of Mallorca, Randa was a bleak and forbidding eminence rising austerely above a sunny plain. The ascent is steep and stony, and the flanks are barren. The Raymond, it was to be ever after the "Mount of the Beloved."

What happened to the mystic on his mountain retreat was known only to God and to Raymond Lull. He seems to have experienced extraordinary manifestations of divine Love, including personal appearances of Christ. After a week's contemplation, during which he passed through a period of intense depression that has been experienced by many mystics, he received inspiration concerning the form and contents of the books he was to write against the errors of the unbelievers.

After this experience, he was universally acclaimed the *Doctor Illuminatus*—illuminated doctor, and after his death, even his enemies made no attempt to deny that he was inspired by God.

The people of Mallorca, proud of Raymond Lull as of the great missionary Junipero Serra, born there five centuries later, have made Mount Randa a place of pilgrimage. At the entrance to Raymond's cave they have erected an inscription:

> This is the place where Blessed Raymond
> Lull retired that he might pray to God.
> As he was in lofty contemplation, there
> appeared to him Jesus crucified, who dis-
> appeared as Raymond embraced him,
> leaving the cross in his arms.

Chapter 4

RAYMOND DESCENDED FROM RANDA
for a period of writing, during which he set down many of the
ideas that had bloomed within him during his period of inspiration. One of the most curious of these was the *Ars Magna,* a system of thought that astounded the Middle Ages. It was a sort of
ingenious scholarly comptometer, by which the problems that
troubled people then—moral, intellectual, even scientific—could
be solved mathematically by transposing numbers and letters
within a series of symbolic diagrams. The *Ars Magna* was
treated with profound respect by the best scholars of the time,
and was itself the subject of many books. Schools of philosophy
were based upon it, and innumerable lectures given to expound
its worth.

Raymond returned to Randa to thank God for his inspiration
and to beg his blessing on his labors. He built a hermitage there,
on the spot where the Franciscan house of Cura now stands,
and devoted himself once more to the rapture of union with his
Beloved.

If Raymond had forgotten the faithful Prince James in the
midst of so much prayer and study, the Prince had not forgotten

him. Rumors of the ex-seneschal's growing fame had reached him at various times, tales of visions and alleged inventions with which to convert unbelievers. James decided to summon Raymond, whom he had not seen in seven years, and see for himself what changes had been wrought in his old friend.

Raymond found the Prince's summons waiting for him when he came down from Randa a second time, and he set out for Montpellier on the mainland of Europe.

It was refreshing to the human nature of Raymond to feel swaying decks under his feet again, and to see the coast of France appear on the distant horizon. There were the three great ports—Lattres, Maguelonne, and Aiguesmortes. There were the forests of masts, the colorful throng of the waterfront, the babel of sailors and traders from every Mediterranean port, as well as from those beyond the Pillars of Hercules. With the princes of Aragon, Raymond Lull loved the land of Montpellier as a second home.

Prince James did not wait until Raymond should be escorted into his royal presence. He went down himself to the palace gates and flung his arms around the thin, coarsely clad man who was so different from the dashing courtier who had been the friend of his youth.

"Raymond, how long it has been! And how very proud of you I am! Wonderful reports have reached me about your powers."

"You do me too great an honor, my Prince," Raymond smiled. Arm in arm, they went into the palace together. Sensing that they must not intrude upon this meeting, the courtiers and servants faded away, leaving the young prince to walk alone with his former tutor.

"I am impatient to hear of your wonderful method to convert the Saracens, Raymond."

"It is more suited to scholars than to warriors such as you, my

Jaime. Yet I will attempt to explain the *Ars Magna* to you. Consider first a circle. The letter A, placed at the center, represents God. The circumference is divided into sixteen parts, each representing an attribute of God. Another circle has the human soul at its center, with its segments the various divisions of human knowledge. . . ."

The Prince listened in awe and confusion as Raymond proceeded deeper into the complexities of his system. Dimly, the young man perceived a great plan of coordination and harmony, but to grasp it was beyond his powers.

"It sounds marvelous, Raymond, and I only wish I could follow it! One thing about it concerns me. You know how many heresies we have in our time, and all novel and unusual ideas become suspect until they are approved. Are you willing to have your works and ideas submitted to a competent judge to receive the Church's approbation?"

Raymond was taken aback. His work heretical? It was incredible! Yet he realized that to a layman such as the prince, the *Ars Magna* must seem almost infinitely profound and complex. "I will gladly do as you suggest," he said, somewhat stiffly.

"Come, come, old friend!" The Prince could not help but smile at the expression on Raymond's face. "If I am to be your champion, then have I not the right to investigate your cause? I am no theologian, however, and so it is only seemly that I entrust the investigation to those more qualified than I. You yourself taught me this way of delegating the work of my kingdom."

"My Jaime, you are right. I confess myself lacking in humility. I have brought with me my books, and you shall submit them to whomever you please."

The Prince fingered his curly beard. "I know a Franciscan scholar at the University of Montpellier, Fray Beltran Berengari. He is a man of wide learning and sympathies, in whom pettiness and pedantry have no part."

"I rejoice that a son of Francis is to examine my work. He will best understand how my feeble words and reason try to follow the flashes of insight the Lord has revealed to me."

The Prince and Raymond then spoke of former days and the doings of old friends. The failure of the crusades was an inevitable topic of conversation, and it gave Raymond the opportunity to bring up his ambitions.

"You have said that you would champion me, my Jaime. I need a powerful friend if I am to accomplish the task I have set myself. You have heard of my hopes to bring the message of the Gospel to the Saracens and Jews. I foresee a new crusade, with sharp minds taking the place of swords. But the training of my intellectual warriors requires that colleges be founded, where priests can learn the languages of the infidels and the customs and traditions that underlie their errors. My own resources have long vanished, Jaime. My estates are the property of Doña Blanca and must be reserved for her and the children. I have only you to turn to for help now."

"Help shall be given you, old friend. Meanwhile, rest here with me while Fray Beltran examines your writings. I have ordered rooms to be prepared for you where you can think and pray in peace. And how I will envy you your solitude!"

So indeed the gentle Prince James envied the inner strength of his old seneschal. In years to come, when his son, another James, would decide like Raymond to follow St. Francis, he would do everything to help him because of Raymond's example.

As he awaited the Church's verdict on his books, Raymond's restless mind conceived new writings. He had been reminded of his children, and now he thought of his son, fatherless in Mallorca. Working with great speed and facility, Raymond wrote his *Doctrine for Boys,* a splendid program of education which covered everything a growing boy ought to know, from hygiene to holiness. It was full of worldly wisdom, gleaned by the author from the adventures of his own tempestuous youth. When he finished this book, he wrote another, *The Order of Chivalry,* regarded by experts as one of the most authoritative works on the subject. Both of these works were dispatched to his young son, tokens of the love borne him by his strange father.

Raymond paced the palace gardens one evening, weary from his writing, when he saw the Prince approach him in a state of nervous excitement.

"Raymond, I have good news for you—although it comes together with sad tidings for me. Fray Beltran has approved your work. What is more, he has written a long report full of admiration of your profundity!"

Raymond's dark eyes flashed. His weariness dropped from him like a discarded mantle. "Excellent! Now my real work can begin!" But then, noting the lines of worry on the Prince's face, he asked, "And what is the sad news, my Jaime?"

The Prince replied with forced calmness, "A courier has brought word that my father has died."

"God grant him rest! This is indeed sad news. I know he had gone to quell a revolt of the Saracens in Valencia. . . . Did he die in battle?"

"No. Fever overtook him at Xativa."

"I see. But then you have at least one comfort—that he had time to prepare his soul. And what splendid things he accomplished during his full life! Has he not laid the foundations of *el magnifico templo* in Palma to sit above the city like a crown for all future generations to marvel at? And has he not won Mallorca for us, as well as many other lands where now the praises of God may be chanted in place of heathen rites?"

"I am consoled by your words, Raymond. He has indeed fought the good fight, and I doubt not that he is crowned with glory for it."

"And what of his dominions?" asked Raymond, with one of those characteristic switches from the spiritual to the practical.

"It will please you to know that I have inherited our dear Mallorca, with this Montpellier of happy memories, and Cerdagne as well. Peter gets Aragon, Valencia, and Catalonia. I feel that these will not satisfy him for long. My brother has inherited the combative spirit of our father."

A page hurried up to James, addressing him as King, and begging his presence in the council chamber. In a few minutes, Raymond found himself alone once more, pondering the fact that his former pupil was now indeed a king, King James II, and wondering whether this new responsibility would affect James' promise about the missionary colleges.

For several weeks, Raymond was left in suspense. Then James summoned him and told him that funds would be made available immediately for the foundation of a college at Miramar on Mallorca—one of the most beautiful sections of the island. The College of the Blessed Trinity was approved by Pope John XXI, and thirteen Franciscan friars were sent there to begin studies in Arabic and kindred subjects.

The Miramar foundation seemed at the time to be the highest achievement in Raymond's life. It was to persist for some sixteen years, but after this it is heard from no more. In the sad poem *Desconhort* (The Disconsolate), written toward the end of his life, Raymond lists the failure of Miramar as one of his greatest disappointments. But the reason for its failure has not been handed down to us.

Raymond remained at Miramar just long enough to see the sons of St. Francis and their tutors well established, and then he was off again on a round of travel. Knowing Pope John XXI to be sympathetic to his missionary ideal, he started off to Rome. It seemed likely that this pontiff would be able to give Raymond a concrete assignment, since the Khan of Tatary had requested that missionaries be sent to him.

Members of the Order of Friars Minor were to carry out this assignment—but they were not graduates of Raymond's school, nor was he himself fated to receive any more assistance from Pope John. In 1277 scaffolding erected in the papal library collapsed on the pontiff, fatally injuring him. This accident also brought about the collapse of Raymond's plans to set out immediately on missionary work. The College of Cardinals did not seem likely to elect a new pope in short order, so Raymond set out for Germany with the idea of rousing some of the kings and princes to the importance of converting the Saracens.

There are no records of the adventures of Raymond Lull throughout the next five years. Traditionally, he traveled down through the Balkans to Armenia, and from there once more to the Holy Land itself. It is possible that he made contact with one of the many caravans that left from Syria for the Far East and traveled into Turkestan. He is known to have gone to Egypt and Morocco, and may have wandered as far as the British Isles. As he roamed, he preached, honing a final keen edge to the sword of the spirit which Fray Ramon had predicted he would carry.

When he finally returned to the court of his patron and ex-pupil, he found that James II had come upon unfortunate times. They sat together one rainy winter night, before a huge stone fireplace in the king's residence at Perpignan, and the ruler once more asked the counsel of his old friend.

"Perhaps what has happened evolves from a flaw in my own

character, Raymond. I am too much like my gentle mother, finding little merit in the intrigues and campaigns that sovereigns rejoice in during these troubled days."

"A peaceful spirit is a fault only in the eyes of the world, Jaime."

The King smiled wryly. "Yet it is in this world that I must live and rule. And if I do not possess the traits of strength that seem to be required, other men who *do* possess them—like my brother Peter—will bring me to grief."

"So it is Peter." Raymond inclined his head, and the glow of the fire shone on his lined forehead. "How well I remember the time—you were both scarcely more than babies—when he demanded all your playthings for himself. I boxed his ears when I found you about to hand them over, and he threatened to poison us both. Alas! His nature has ever been that of a bully."

"My father on his deathbed charged him strictly to respect my inheritance. But even this sacred appeal made no impression on him. Peter cast covetous eyes on my lands, especially Montpellier, and demanded that I become his vassal. In the end I was forced to yield, weakling that I am. Just three years ago I made formal recognition of him as my liege lord. But not even this satisfied him. He demanded another humiliating obeisance in Palma eleven months later. Now he has spread his dominions into Africa and captured the city of Constantine. Recently he was crowned king of Sicily, and he has begun to speak of himself as the new Alexander."

"An Alexander!" snorted Raymond.

"He has conquered me," James said sadly. "I fear I am about to succumb to despair. You must guide me, Raymond, for you have ever been a man of courage while I have had to lean upon others. Tell me, why must things go well for a wicked king like my brother, while I, who labored to bring good to my people, receive only a legacy of sorrow and failure?"

"Another king asked this question, my Jaime, and God gave him an answer. Remember the song that David sang:

> Be not incensed because of evildoers, nor
> envious of those who work iniquity;
>
> For like grass they will soon wither, and like
> green herbs they will fade.
>
> Hope in the Lord and do good, that you may
> dwell in the land and enjoy security. . . .
>
> Rest in the Lord, and hope in him. Be not
> incensed because of him who prospers in his
> undertakings, because of one who plots evil things. . . .
>
> For evildoers shall be destroyed; but they
> who hope in the Lord shall possess the land. . . .
>
> I have seen the wicked man in his pride, spreading
> himself like a leafy cedar.
>
> And I passed by, and lo, he was no more; and I
> sought him, but he was not to be found.
>
> Mark the upright and consider the just man:
> for there is a progeny for the man of peace.
>
> But sinners shall all be destroyed.

You must continue to hope, my Jaime, knowing that God's justice finally renders to each man his due."

James sighed. "The progeny of the man of peace. . . . Francis of Assisi received the latter title, did he not, Raymond? And he, too, seemed to fail."

"As you and I, Jaime," Raymond interposed.

The king smiled. "As you and I. Yet his progeny have multiplied and his messengers carry God's word to all peoples. Perhaps it is God's will that we learn from his example. Raymond, my dear friend, I am not a saint. But perhaps I can learn patience, at least, from the Poor Man of Assisi."

"And perhaps," Raymond said, "the teacher can follow the example of the erstwhile pupil. Our lives are threads in the design of Providence, and at the moment, they run dark. But the end has not yet come, Jaime, and you and I must wait."

Chapter 5

THERE COMES A TIME IN THE LIVES of many creative men when all experience seems to ripen and call for expression in words. Such a time came to Raymond Lull around the year 1284, after he had left the troubled King James and retired to a quiet retreat in Montpellier. It was there that he composed the work for which he is best remembered, *Blanquerna*.

Named for its chief character, the work is the first novel to be written in any of the Romance languages. Intensely allegorical, it can fairly be described as a kind of *Pilgrim's Progress* of Franciscan ideals—not for any specific Franciscan teaching encompassed, but rather for the over-all Franciscanism of its attitude to life and human destiny. Some of its metaphors recall St. Bonaventure's *Journey of the Mind to God,* written some thirty years earlier, which Raymond had certainly read. But *Blanquerna* has a freshness all its own. Its eloquent praises of love and its emphasis on simplicity are essentially Franciscan, as is also its glorification of holy Poverty.

The hero wanders through the world, experiencing many adventures and concluding that virtue lies in solitude and contemplation. After many allegorical experiences, he becomes a monk —then an abbot. Appointed bishop, Blanquerna reforms his diocese according to the principles of the eight Beatitudes. His fame for sanctity and wise administration becomes so great that he is finally elected pope. From the chair of St. Peter, he undertakes the reform and sanctification of the entire world.

Through all the years since he was first elected abbot, Blanquerna has been secretly yearning for the life of a hermit. In the end, he renounces the papacy and departs for a hermitage on a high mountain. At this part of the book, two chapters are introduced which are really distinct literary works composed many years previously. They are *The Book of the Lover and the Beloved* and the *Art of Contemplation*. In the last chapter, the Emperor arrives and asks to be directed to Blanquerna's hermitage, where he wishes to join him. And there the story ends.

The Book of the Lover and the Beloved might almost be an adaptation of a poem written by St. Francis to describe his experience on La Verna. A classic of mysticism, it shows its author to have been an active-contemplative like the followers of the Poverello. Nowhere is the active life looked down upon; and just as St. Francis came down from the heights of La Verna to mingle with men in the marketplace, so the Lover in Raymond Lull's work is led by the Beloved from the crests of contemplation down into the world's arena, to work there and do good.

There is a prophetic element in *Blanquerna* which adds to its appeal. Ten years after the book was written, Pope Celestine V, who had been a simple hermit, abdicated and wished to return to his monastery. He had been warned by Jacopone da Todi against the wiles of ambitious men, and it was his fate to die in prison. He became an object of Dante's scorn for the "great refusal" of responsibility. Raymond was to approach him long after writing the book, but the frail and bewildered pontiff was unable to help. Pope Celestine was canonized by Clement V in 1313.

In 1285, Raymond went to Rome again to enlist the aid of Pope Martin IV. It must have seemed to the pilgrim of love that the old pattern of frustration was repeating itself; for just as he reached the Eternal City, the pope died in Perugia. Prudently, Raymond utilized the hiatus of the papal elections to attend a General Chapter of the Dominicans in Bologna, but had little success there in promoting his missionary plans.

When he returned to Rome and sought audience with the new pope, Honorius IV, he was received at once and treated with cordial respect. The new pope was a feeble octogenarian, but nonetheless a patron of universities and enthusiastically in agreement with Raymond's ideals for the teaching of oriental languages to missionaries. Raymond's joy can be imagined when Honorius told him that he would be pleased to help Raymond found schools in Rome and Paris. While in Rome, Raymond wrote *The Book of the Tatar and the Christian,* which followed his philosophy of allowing the infidel to expound all of his own tenets of belief and objections to the Christian faith. At the close of the book, the monk Blanquerna appears again to solve the Tatar's difficulties and prove that Catholicism is the only faith capable of logical demonstration.

To that period also belongs a quaint work of verse, *The Hundred Names of God.* The preface says that in the Koran, the Saracens hold that there are ninety-nine names of God, and that he who knows the hundredth will know all things. "Wherefore," says the author, "I make this book of the Hundred Names of God; and since it does not follow that I know all things, I do this to reprove the Saracens' false opinions." The modern mind sees this as an odd approach to apologetics; but there is no doubting the sincerity and single-mindedness of the author.

Lull had considerable influence with Honorius IV, and the pontiff sought and followed his advice in many matters. It was on Raymond's advice, for example, that the pope disbanded the spurious religious order of the Apostles, and intensified missionary activity among the Moors. Had he reigned longer than two years he would almost certainly have planned a Franciscan crusade for Africa with Miramar as his model.

When Raymond journeyed to Paris, he was welcomed by the University Chancellor himself, who had already received letters of commendation from Pope Honorius. But even before this, Raymond's fame had spread throughout the schools; the doctors were well aware that the new courses in Hebrew and Arabic were in response to Raymond's appeals to the Holy Father.

The months that followed were full of feverish activity for Raymond, who seems to have been driving himself mercilessly in pursuit of his goal. He wrote three books, two of which were brief: *The Dispute Between a Believer and an Unbeliever* and *The Book of the Fourteen Articles,* both dealing with apologetics; but the third book was a great romantic novel called *Felix,* or *The Book of Marvels.* The hero of this lengthy tale is the boy Felix, who is sent by his father to see the great world and learn its marvels. He is to record what he learns, so that on his return home the boy and his father can assemble the book together. There are ten parts to the book: on God, the angels, elements, heavens, plants, metals, beasts, man, paradise, and hell. Since one part alone, that on man, has 72 chapters, we can only stand in amazement and awe at Felix's unflagging energy and powers of observation—to say nothing of those possessed by the author of such an encyclopedia.

The atmosphere pervading the University of Paris at that time was one of dissension and suspicion. There was an uneasy truce between the orthodox schoolmen and the proponents of the doctrine of the Spanish Moor Averroes, introduced over a century ago. Every new philosopher—including Raymond—could expect to be scrutinized mercilessly. But Raymond's *Art* passed even this rigorous examination, and he was given the title of "Master," which carried with it the right to teach in the university.

The Dominican Chapter was held in Paris at Whitsuntide, 1286, and Raymond again carried his case before the blackfriars. But once more he was doomed to disappointment. Other matters occupied the Dominicans, who were additionally suspicious of his non-Thomistic *Art*. His friend Raymund of Peñafort had died in 1275, and there was no one to take his place as a sympathizer with Raymond's cause.

He came away from the Chapter disappointed, but not dispirited. And as it happened, Providence placed another source of potential aid before him almost at once.

Raymond had heard that the exiled King James II of Mallorca was at the court of King Philip the Fair of France, his sister's son. Nothing was more natural than that his "dear Jaime" should arrange an interview between Raymond and Philip. Philip had been assisting James to rally forces against Peter, and he was a coldly practical man. But the ex-courtier Raymond had no difficulty finding the right note to strike with this ambitious monarch.

"It is a great joy to me to greet your Majesty," Raymond said suavely, "not only on your own illustrious account, but for the sake of your noble mother, the gracious Elizabeth of blessed memory."

The king's severe face softened. "Ah, yes. You knew my sainted mother. Do you know, Raymond, I was her favorite son? She used to say I was very like her father, James the Conqueror, and that some day I would be as great a ruler as he."

The gentleness drained from his face as the thought of glory blazed from the king's blue eyes. "Who knows what day may be dawning for France? But you must let me hear of your mission and what it is you seek of me."

"I seek nothing for myself, your Majesty. I ask only for help in spreading the Kingdom of Christ among the heathen." He drew out a parchment from a fold in his garment. "I have set out in this parchment my plan for colleges for the training of missionaries, and His Holiness Pope Honorius has blessed the project by founding a school at Rome and one in the University here. If your Majesty would have other such schools established in the kingdom of France, the menace from the East would be forever removed and a bloodless victory won for the Cross. Your good mother may have been right. You may be destined to be the last, the *victorious* Crusader-King."

"Ah, Raymond, you scarce know how your vision moves me. Would that I had ten men such as you at my side to work for France! But you must know that war clouds loom over us already, blowing from England across her puppet, Flanders. And as yet the storm over Sicily has not cleared. But you have our royal word. As soon as these urgent affairs of state are happily settled you shall have your colleges, endowed and set up under the patronage of Philip of France. And may God prosper your holy work!"

Richer by promises, at least, Raymond left Paris in the spring of 1287 and returned to his beloved Montpellier. He set to work teaching in the schools and writing a simpler version of the *Art,* which he called *The Art of Finding Truth*. He attended a General Chapter of the Friars Minor, before which he set the same projects that had been rejected earlier by the Dominicans in Paris. He must have received a sympathetic hearing, because he made ready with renewed zest to go to Rome and report to his friend, Pope Honorius.

Just as he was about to embark, news reached him that Honorius had died. Raymond resignedly went back to his lecturing while six months of disputation occupied the College of Cardinals. Finally, in February of 1288, the joyful news came that the first Franciscan pope had been elected—Jerome Masci, the general of the order, who chose the name of Nicholas IV.

It was typical of Raymond's incredible energy that he could make a short stay in Genoa on his way to Rome in order to translate *The Art of Finding Truth* into Arabic. What to most people would be a monumental labor was to him a mere by-product of his dynamic spirit.

He was welcomed by the new Pontiff with brotherly affection, but it was made clear to him that the papal attentions were engaged at that time in mediating the Sicilian wars. However, Nicholas IV soon directed his attention to the missions to such an extent that he became one of their greatest promoters. During his short reign of four years he wrote no less than 2,000 letters and other documents dealing exclusively with the missions of the Franciscan and Dominican friars in non-Christian lands.

Was Raymond beginning to sense a disadvantage in his solitary position? His tentative alliance with the Dominicans had failed, and he seemed temperamentally drawn toward the Franciscans. Still, he had formally allied himself with no religious order up to this time and his uncertain status was proving a hindrance to success. But the worldly wisdom which led Raymond to importune kings and popes on behalf of his plans failed at this time to inspire him to join the sons of St. Francis. He was attracted to them, he was part of them in spirit, but he was not formally one of them. And therein lay the difficulty.

Raymond gained the friendship of the new Minister General

of the Franciscans, Raymund Gaufredi, and attended another General Chapter of the order. Soon afterward he returned to Montpellier.

A novel idea had occurred to him, quite revolutionary for that time. He proposed to write in the vernacular for the ordinary people "so that those who know no Latin may have an art and doctrine of Love." Evidently he hoped that other writers would follow his example and write in their mother tongue. Along the same line of popularization, he simplified the style and presentation of some of his books. "Subtleties we avoid, as far as we can, that this book may be comprehended," he says in the prolog to *The Book of St. Mary,* a book of devotion for ordinary people.

Other books written by Raymond at this time include *The Art of Loving the Good* and *Questions Asked by a Certain Friar Minor,* which may have been a synopsis of questions asked by Gaufredi and answers given by Lull. The Franciscan Minister General certainly examined a number of Lull's works and probably also questioned him on his teaching and missionary plans; because in letters dated October 26, 1290, he gave Raymond letters of introduction to all the houses of the order in the provinces of Rome, Apulia, and Sicily.

The time now seemed auspicious for another visit to Rome. The situation in Sicily had eased, and Raymond, remembering Pope Nicholas's promise, seized his new opportunity. He prepared a paper to present to the Holy Father, setting out what he considered to be the chief obstacles to the conquest of the Holy Land, and urging the Pope to seek to unify the bickering military orders of the Knights Templars and Knights of St. John, whose dissensions were undermining the Christian conquests in Palestine.

58

Armed with this cogent analysis, he presented himself once more to Nicholas IV, and was greeted warmly. But the Pope listened to Raymond's elaborate plans with a preoccupied smile. "You have summed up the need for missionary work brilliantly, Raymond our son," Nicholas said, "and we promise to do all we can to sustain you in your heaven-directed labor. As a matter of fact, your plan ties in perfectly with one of our own. We are even now planning a new crusade! And if by God's grace the army of Christendom should triumph, the way will be made clear for your missionary work among the infidels."

These words, delivered with gentle enthusiasm, assaulted Raymond's consciousness like a blow. Frustration and bitterness surged up like a dark tide within him, and he stood before the Holy Father as a man struck suddenly blind and deaf. Nicholas noticed nothing, and eventually the audience came to an end. Raymond recovered himself as he was led away by the papal chamberlain, and the recovery was worse than the momentary oblivion he had experienced.

It had been made crystal clear to him: the work of the sword came first in Nicholas's mind, and only when the Saracens had been subdued by force would the Pope consider Raymond's crusade of love. He had been forced to put off once more the work promised to his Beloved.

Raymond was now an old man. He knew that there was no more time to be spent patiently waiting for others to assist him. The task was his, and if need be he would undertake it alone.

Chapter 6

DARK CLOUDS WERE MASSING OVER the sea as Raymond turned from Rome along the Via Aureliana to take the coast road towards Genoa.

Brassy sunlight glared down on huge broken shapes, lying half obscured by rank shrubbery. The outskirts of the decaying Eternal City seemed to be littered with empty ruins. No sound of a human voice reached the ears of the man trudging the dusty road, but only the screeching of seabirds wheeling restlessly over the skeletons of broken aqueducts.

The traveler met not a single soul. "They are all resting," he told himself. "If only I could rest. But I must not. I must press on, following you, Lord, for I do not know how to offer you my failure. I must—I *will*—offer you success. I will succeed at my crusade and then I will lay it at your feet all golden and triumphant, and I will—"

A violent gust of wind swept grit up from the road and into the eyes of the traveler. He paused to wipe his face with his sleeve, and when his eyes cleared he saw the seagulls were circling around his head. He watched them uneasily, silhouetted against the inflamed sky, while the wind whipped his coarse robe about his body. The birds' cries had a strange mocking note.

They flew lower and lower, until their wings almost seemed to brush his head.

"Lord, why do the very creatures turn to torment me?" A black wing grazed his shoulder, and the bird trailed a raucous scream as it swooped high into the darkening sky. "I thought I knew the birds of the sea, Lord. But wherefore these black gulls, which I have never seen before? Are there black gulls, Lord?"

Three of the creatures dived at once, and he waved his staff threateningly at them. They fled, jeering, and a rumble of thunder swept in from the sea and echoed among the ruins.

"The voice of the Lord is upon the waters. The God of majesty has thundered. Mighty is the voice of the Lord! The voice of the Lord is full of majesty. . . . " The psalm faded on his lips and his steps faltered. He clung to the staff more tightly and closed his eyes against the blast of wind and dust that struck him. A moaning sound came from the branches of a gnarled tree beside the road, and when he opened his eyes he made his way to a stone beside its trunk and sat down.

Thunder pealed again. He declaimed: "The voice of the Lord breaks the cedars; the voice of the Lord shatters the cedars of Lebanon! The voice of the Lord sends forth flames of fire! The voice of the Lord twists the oaks and strips bare the forests; and in his temple all cry: Glory!"

A great flash of lightning that seemed to reach almost from horizon to horizon lit up the landscape; almost simultaneously there was a titanic clap of thunder. "The Lord sits above the flood, and the Lord presides as a king forever!" He repeated the last word over and over again, savoring it as a toothsome morsel at a banquet. "Your glory is forever, and I am going to magnify your glory before the unbelievers despite the rebuffs and indifference shown to me by your servants. I am going to do it, Lord!"

He struggled to his feet and began to stride firmly down the road into the teeth of the approaching storm. "I am on my way to magnify your glory, Lord! I am on my way—" He slowed his pace and glanced frantically from one side of the road to the other. "I am on my way—" he repeated. The road before him was strange and dim, its dusty surface pocked now with the first large raindrops that began to splatter down. He said once more, "I am on my way—" and then sobbed aloud in terror.

He could not remember where he was going.

A countryman, hurrying home with his balky donkey, found the traveler standing in the middle of the storm. By his garb, he knew Raymond was a scholar and a pilgrim, so he cheerfully urged the sodden wayfarer to accompany him to his hut for the night.

"God's blessing be upon you," Raymond managed to mutter, and within a few minutes he was sitting before a small warm fire while the countryman's wife bustled to prepare dinner for the guest.

Although he was a simple man, the host was prudent enough to speak little. Nor did he presume to question why his strange guest should have stood weeping in the mud of the Genoa road, with tears and raindrops mingled on his frightened face.

Raymond resumed his journey on the following day. The confusion had vanished with sleep, but the fear remained deep within him. Many times during his life, when he had followed a humor that seemed inexplicable to his companions, Raymond Lull had been called a madman. But then the epithet had been a jest.

"Am I losing my reason, Lord?" he asked. "Lord, do not forsake me now! Jesus, I love you! Let me serve you with this mind. How can there be honor for you in the cries of insanity?

63

Jesus, source of love, have mercy!"

He traveled for several days more, coming upon Genoa at mid-day. He had been there only once before, and had almost forgotten what manner of city it was. The swaying myriad masts in the gulf told of its thriving commerce. Its courageous sailors had traded all along the coast of Barbary, fighting its pirates and taking Moorish towns by storm. The brave Genoese dared to sail beyond the Pillars of Hercules, into the great ocean that was said to swarm with supernatural monsters. Superstitious souls claimed that if a ship sailed far to westward, it would drop off into a fathomless abyss. Raymond knew this was nonsense. It was far more likely that land lay to the west, perhaps peopled by simple inhabitants who would welcome the message of the Gospels.

Abstractedly, Raymond thought he would have to write a book about this novel theory. Still musing on the uncharted west, he passed through the Porta Lanterna into the ringing streets.

It was not long before someone recognized him, and the word soon spread abroad. Here was the man who had been visited by God on a holy mountain, like the blessed Francis of Assisi! Perhaps he had come to work miracles among them! Beggars, townswomen, idlers, and children began to press close to him, shouting and calling out.

Raymond stood in silence. But the old adventurer's smile played over his lips.

"Silence!" yelled a burly man, dressed in the clothes of a sailor. "Stop your clattering tongues! *Il Santo* wishes to speak to us!"

"No, no, my good people," said the discomfited Raymond. "In truth I am no saint, but a miserable sinner and a pilgrim for Love's sake."

A little girl piped: "But we heard that you would work some

miracles for us! I never saw a miracle before."

Raymond laughed. "Alas, little one, I work no miracles. But I would attempt one mighty deed. I would sail in one of your boats to Africa. And once there, I would set the infidel hearts on fire with the love of God! I would dare to do more than the crusades did. I would lead Africa captive to Love! I would sweep thousands of Moors into the very arms of God. . . . "

He caught the look of amazement that spread over the faces of the people. "Forgive me, dear friends. I do not speak for pride or foolishness, although I am the very Fool of Love. Yet such a mission has been the goal of my life. Will you take me in one of your ships that I may make the name of the Beloved known among the infidels?"

"Yes! Yes!" they shouted. One captain after another cried out that his vessel was at the command of the pilgrim. A great wrangle broke out as to who would have the privilege of carrying the holy man on so great a mission.

It was finally decided that he would sail on the *Santo Donato,* which was scheduled to leave for Tunis the day after tomorrow. As the matter was settled, Raymond began to tremble so much that an old woman shouted that he was surely about to have a vision.

"Nay, not a vision. I am only weary and hungry." The dark eyes glanced nervously into the air above the crowd. "And the birds trouble me somewhat with their ceaseless circling."

"What birds?" asked the child. Raymond looked at her narrowly. "I don't see any birds," she insisted.

"Come away with us, Master Raymond," said a prosperous looking merchant heartily.

His wife added, "Your journey has fatigued you. We will put a quiet suite of rooms at your disposal so that you may rest before your journey."

Raymond accompanied them to their home, scarcely speaking a dozen words until he was left alone on a small balcony overlooking the sea. The bright waters of the harbor seemed oddly suffused with mist, and the mist permeated the streets and dimmed even the corners of his spacious room. But it did not conceal the birds. . . .

When the master of the house came to summon his guest to dinner an hour or so later, he gave a cry of dismay and rushed out onto the balcony. Raymond lay unconscious on the tiles. He was put to bed, and a doctor was sent for immediately. All through the night, Raymond wept and cried the name of his Beloved. A mysterious fever burned within him, and he made incoherent demands upon his frightened host and hostess, falling at last into a profound stupor near dawn.

He lay almost as a corpse through the next day and night, and the *Santo Donato* sailed without him. Gossip flew through the houses and taverns of Genoa. The holy man was seized with a strange illness! No, he was possessed by Satan—for had he not been accused of heresy by the Dominican professors? No, he was really wrapt in the throes of a new ecstasy! On the contrary, he had gone mad and was raving that the birds of hell were come to carry him off!

On Quinquagesima Sunday, he begged to be carried to the Dominican church for Mass. Afterwards, he was brought to the friars' infirmary, where he said that he was dying. The friars were greatly agitated by his presence. They could not refuse to give him shelter because of the sympathetic mood of the townspeople. But it would be very embarrassing indeed if this singular, somewhat notorious man should die on their hands.

"If only the prior had not gone to Perugia!" they fretted.

The brother infirmarian came running into the hall where the friars were gathered. "Father Dominic help us! He's asking to be clothed in our habit!"

There was a general gasp of dismay.

Fray Benedetto, upon whose shoulders responsibility rested during the absence of the prior, took the Mallorquin bull by the horns.

"Be at peace, Master Raymond," he said to the sick man. "Now what can I do to help you?"

"Bless me, Father, for I have sinned!"

"Yes, yes," the friar said soothingly. "We have heard your confession."

"I am dying," said Raymond, rising up suddenly upon his elbows and fixing Fray Benedetto with his burning gaze. "A short time ago a brilliant star appeared in this room. And coming from it, I heard the voice of the Lord ordering me to ask for the habit of a Dominican tertiary."

The friar's mouth opened in astonishment. "Indeed! Yet you must know, Master Raymond, that I cannot accede to such an unusual request. There has been no postulancy. We know your reputation for learning, of course, but still—"

"You refuse me?" Raymond demanded.

"Only the prior could authorize such an unusual investiture. He is in Perugia and will not return for two weeks."

Raymond sank back into the bed, pale and blue-lipped. The brother infirmarian regarded his superior with alarm. But a moment later, the sick man's eyes opened and restlessly roved the room. Finally they came to rest on the knotted cord hanging from the ceiling beside his bed. It was used to summon the infirmarian.

"Father Francis!" Raymond suddenly exclaimed. "I know that *you* will not refuse me! Your generosity will pardon my monstrous defection. You will receive me and bear me on your seraph's wings to the feet of the Love for whom you died!"

So Great a Lover

Hope gleamed once more on Fray Benedetto's face. "You wish to be taken to the Franciscans?"

"At once," Raymond answered.

And so the townspeople bore him to the house of the Friars Minor, who with the tactfulness of their founder promised to receive him into their order as soon as he was well enough. "I thank you. I thank you," he said weakly, and was borne away to recover at the house of the merchant who had originally befriended him.

Strength and reason gradually returned to him, and so did the recollection of his interrupted journey. One day, while still too weak to walk, he had himself and his books brought down to the quayside when news reached him that a galley was about to embark for Tunis.

His exasperated friends dashed down the dock and brought him back under protest. He submitted temporarily. But when he heard of another boat leaving for the same port a few days later, he insisted that he was well enough to travel and demanded to be put aboard. The townspeople decided to let him go. The change and the sea air might do him good, and if he stayed, he might very well worry himself into a relapse.

The sailors received Raymond aboard the *San Bernardo* with hearty shouts of welcome. They bore the feeble missionary onto the deck with their strong arms, made him comfortable in the lee of the cabin, and set sail.

Strength seemed to surge back into his worn body as the craft pointed her prow toward Africa. His nervous illness melted away like spring ice in a running stream, and the rise and fall of the sea seemed like the pulsing of a mighty heart full of love. Cradled on that heart, he felt his confidence return. He was once more in pursuit of the one true Love. God had rescued him from the depths.

So Great a Lover

On such a small craft, a mere hundred feet long, it was easy to get to know every sailor and passenger aboard. The sailors gladly imparted to him what lore of the stars had come to them through oriental astrologers; while he, with his intuitive genius, sifted the facts from the fables to produce scientific results. He taught them to check their courses by the stars, and eventually he was to have the title of "Navigator" added to the many honors accorded him by posterity.

From the merchant pasengers, Raymond learned many valuable lessons on the customs of the Saracens—their social taboos, their forms of etiquette, and the most likely ways that he might gain a hearing with them. These, in the practical affairs of his apostolate, would be almost as useful as the books and sermons he had prepared. For a dream was of no use if it could not be translated into the rugged reality.

Two merchants he met on this voyage were later to play a most important part in his life—and death. Their names were Luigi de Pastorga and Stefano Colombo.

As soon as the ship docked at Tunis, Raymond set about his business. He acquired a murky, one-room hovel to serve as his headquarters, then went at once to the bazaar to mingle with the people. With tact and courtesy, he found out the things he wanted to know: the political situation of the moment, the names of the officials and scholars with whom he would have to deal, the meeting places of the local intelligentsia.

After reconnoitering the battlefield, he presented himself to the Moslem scholars, briefly sketched his qualifications, and invited them to a philosophical debate. "We will debate the merits of our respective religions according to the principles of logic, science, and history. And if, at the end, I find your beliefs to be true and my own false, I promise to embrace the religion of the Prophet."

An astonished murmuring arose among the Moorish wise men. What manner of Christian was this, who did not seek to ridicule them, nor crudely force his dogma upon them? They did not know what to make of Raymond; but his sheepskin from the University of Paris was proof enough that he was no unlettered friar. His gray beard and venerable mien belied the coarse cloth of his garments, and the salient wit with which he responded to their guarded questions evoked hope that he might be a worthy opponent in debate.

As he awaited their decision apprehensively, Raymond prayed to his Beloved to accept the offering of his life's work. If the Moslems refused to debate with him, he would have no alternative but to preach in the bazaar—and he knew from bitter experience that the esoteric niceties of logic and his Art made no impression upon the stubborn prejudices of the ignorant. He had counted on the oriental's love for arguing—whether over the price of a carpet or the relation of God and man—to open the way for him. It turned out that he was not to be disappointed.

"We accept your challenge, Master Raymond Lull," the oldest of the scholars said. "We shall meet with you, on days that will be agreed upon, and continue the contest of intellect until you are won over to the cause of Islam."

"It will be as God wills," said Raymond, bowing, and he left them to prepare for the first of the debates.

The Moorish teachers and scholars began their first mental joust with Raymond full of confidence and pride. But the debate on the necessity for man's redemption, which Raymond had chosen to open the contest, proved to them that their Christian opponent was not only worthy of them but possibly destined to be victorious. They met with him three times a week in a cool, high-arched chamber adjacent to the largest mosque in Tunis.

One by one they stood up to attack the truths of Christianity, and one by one Raymond vanquished them and sent them shuffling off in confusion.

The trouble with this Christian devil, they told each other, was that he was as familiar with the tenets of Mohammedanism as they were themselves. He knew all the inconsistencies and inadequacies that were inherent in Islam—the reliance on the senses, the stultifying bonds of fanaticism and unreason toward which they themselves had felt a resentment. He was able to seize on these things and twist them to his own purpose. If one were not cautious, this Christian would almost convince one to swear fidelity to the religion of Issus ben Miriam!

Raymond was elated at his obvious success. He had no illusions that these learned ones would immediately seek baptism. But he hoped that, given time, God's grace would have a chance to work within them.

The year was 1291, and Raymond had been in Tunis for only a few months when news arrived of the Saracen victory at Acre. The last Christian stronghold in the Holy Land had fallen, and there were no signs that the Christian rulers would implement a new crusade to attempt its recapture. Poor Nicholas IV wore himself out in fruitless attempts to raise a new army, only to die a year later, heartbroken with frustration.

But Raymond's crusade of the intellect took a far different turn. After over a year of brilliant campaigning, he made his first converts among the Moorish wise men. But his success was almost to prove his undoing. One of the doctors, alarmed at the results of Raymond's activities, went to the Caliph with news that Islam was in danger of extermination. He demanded the stipulated penalty for those who spoke against the Prophet—a cruel death.

Armed men were sent to apprehend Raymond and imprison

him, while the Caliph held council. Was it true that this Christian had made fools of the wise men of Tunis? If he had done so, was the response of the wise men, it was only because of a diabolical technique which enabled him to turn their own arguments against them. The Christian was clearly guilty, and there remained only the task of sentencing him.

"Torture and death to the Christian!" cried most of the council. But an influential minority suggested that to kill this brilliant scholar who had bested them in intellectual combat would be to admit to the world that Islam was as benighted as Raymond said that it was. Banishment would rid them of the nuisance but preserve their prestige.

Crouched in a dark and filthy cell, Raymond could hear the raging of a mob outside. Fanatics were inflaming the people with hatred toward him, urging that he be hauled out of the prison at once and torn limb from limb. The tumult was stilled only when the muezzin called them to prayer from the newly built Kasba Mosque, and the sudden silence seemed almost more menacing than the screaming of a few minutes ago.

His jailer had told him that the Caliph's council was in session, and that he would be condemned to torture and death. His dream of dying for his Beloved would be realized. But he was troubled once more at his inability to offer success. He had positive proof now that his crusade of the intellect would work; if only he had the scores of followers he had dreamed of, men like the Franciscans he had trained in Miramar. . . .

His reverie was shattered by a commotion outside his cell. The door was flung open and he was dragged into the dazzling sunlight. Courageously, he braced himself for the final act, the immolation of himself for the love of Christ. Dark, ferocious faces were thrust into his, mouthing insults and spitting at him. Stones bounded off his body. He was being dragged along—but where?

The street began to descend and the odor of the sea hit his nostrils.

A group of Genoese sailors broke through the mob of Moors, and Raymond was half dragged, half carried aboard their ship. Hurling epithets at the crowd, the seamen placed the battered missionary under an awning in the after part of the ship. He lay there among the bundles of merchandise; silent and unmoving, until the mob faded away.

Dimly, he heard a merchant complain to one of the crew that trade relations between Tunis and Mallorca, to which this meddling preacher belonged, had always been friendly. A pity these do-gooders could not leave well enough alone. If this one had a compulsion to be murdered, it was his own affair; but the merchant expressed the hope that the preacher would pick a better time and place.

With the heat of the afternoon, work ceased and silence settled over the quayside. Raymond felt his strength begin to return, and he was once more troubled by the fact that the work he had begun so successfully must now be interrupted. Perhaps if he were able to get to the house of Habib Abdullah, one of his converts, he could secrete himself until tempers cooled and resume his activities in a more circumspect manner.

He waited until the sailors had all left, then slipped off the ship and made his way cautiously back into the center of town. As he was rounding a corner, he heard an angry snarling that could only mean that the mob was on the prowl again. Some other poor soul was being hounded down.

He shrank back into the shadows just in time. "Kill the insolent blasphemer! Kill the infidel dog who dares return to mock the Prophet!" A shouting horde boiled out of a side street, pursuing their hapless victim. To his surprise, Raymond saw it was a Christian merchant, dressed in gray like himself and with a flowing beard like his own.

Frantic with terror, the man was finally cornered. "I am not Master Raymond!" he screamed. "I tell you I am not he—only a poor merchant come to do business among you. Come to the *funduq* and I will prove it to you! You are making a terrible mistake, and the Bey will have your lives if you harm me!"

Muttering, the crowd fell back. At that moment, a squad of men-at-arms clattered up to disperse them. The merchant, his eyes still bulging with fright, limped off.

Raymond had seen enough to convince him of the uselessness of resuming his crusade at the present time. It was clear to him that prudence demanded that he leave Tunis. He drew his hood over his head and went sadly back to the harbor, creeping unnoticed into his place in the boat.

Completely overcome by exhaustion and his injuries, he fell sound asleep. When he awoke, the little vessel was speeding through the moonlit sea to the tune of an old Genoese chanty.

Chapter 7

HE DISEMBARKED AT NAPLES SOME time toward the close of 1292. It had been two years since he had done any real writing, and he was anxious to take up the pen again before he journeyed off anew. Installing himself in a small monastery overlooking the Bay of Naples, he began to set down some of the conclusions he had drawn during his missionary activity.

As always, he was obsessed by the divine admonition that there be one fold and one shepherd. He seized upon the fact that, up to the time of Pope John XXI, it was the Nestorian missionaries who evangelized the greater part of Asia; and it was owing to their penetration that the Mongols were favorably disposed towards all Christians, even to the extent of sending requests to Rome for more missionaries. The Nestorians, believing in two separate Persons in Christ, flourished for six centuries in Central Asia; small pockets of them still exist in Kurdistan, while the Syrian church still preserves Nestorian doctrines.

Raymond realized that if the Saracens were to sweep the Tatars into their sphere of influence and subjugate the Nestorian Christians of Asia, Catholic Europe would be a mere isolated peninsula, lying helplessly under the dangling scimitar of Islam. It was in an effort to arouse Christendom to the proximity of disaster that Raymond composed *The Book of the Five Wise Men.* The five protagonists are Roman, Greek, Nestorian, and Jacobite Catholics—plus a Moslem. The book is a carefully constructed controversy, in which each viewpoint is presented and played against the other four. It is remarkable as a revelation of the divided state of Christendom during the thirteenth century, and one of the most cogent arguments ever written for the necessity of Christian unity.

When he completed this work, he began another: *A Petition for the Conversion of the Heathen.* While he was still working on it, word reached him that after twenty-seven months of temporizing and bickering, the College of Cardinals had finally elected a successor to Nicholas IV. He was Pietro of Morrone, a virtuous and innocent Benedictine hermit, who had been elected to dissolve a stalemate between warring factions of the Sacred College. The new pope, who was over eighty, had strenuously resisted his election; but the cardinals had convinced him that it was the Divine Will that he ascend the Chair of Peter.

To Raymond, the saintly old man must have seemed at first to be the very incarnation of Blanquerna. But Celestine V, as he chose to style himself, was to prove a lamb among the wolves. He lived in Naples, where venal cardinals and the ambitious King Charles II of Naples used him shamefully to forward their own ends. When Raymond presented his *Petition,* the Pope was too confused by the intrigue around him to pay any serious attention to it. Baffled and wretched in the midst of such corruption after nearly fifty years of cloistered calm, Pope Celestine abdicated after five months. The year was 1294.

Eleven days afterward, Benedetto Gaetani succeeded him as Boniface VIII, a man of energetic character, with a wide knowl-

edge of canon and civil law and long experience in ecclesiastical
and political life. Raymond resolved to try his luck with the new
Holy Father.

At some time during this period, Raymond also finally decided
to seek admittance into the Third Order of St. Francis. It is puz-
zling why he delayed so long taking the step, especially in view
of his frenzied plea for the habit during his illness in Genoa.
Perhaps he realized that his actions at that time smacked of the
irrational, and postponed joining the Franciscans until his sanity
could no longer be disputed.

Early in 1295 he went to ravaged Rome, which had once
again become the seat of the papacy. His patriarchal appearance
and single-minded devotion to his plan for converting the
heathen earned him nothing but scorn and suspicion from the
cynical courtiers of Boniface; but worse was in store for him.
The pope was entirely immersed in temporal affairs. Trouble
had flared up in Sicily again; there was unrest in Tuscany and
Florence; Genoa and Florence were at war. Moreover, Philip
the Fair of France, who was a patron of Raymond's was a dead-
ly enemy of the Pope. It is hardly surprising that Raymond's
Petition was once more rejected. As the old man turned his steps
from Rome towards Assisi, the chill *tramontana* wind struck
deep within him. The world had become a cold, unsympathetic
place, and the indifference of men to his Beloved lay on his
heart heavy as frost.

But a golden spring awaited him in Assisi, where he was finally received into the Franciscan ranks. For a time he refreshed
his soul in the beautiful Umbrian hills, recalling the time—so far
distant from him now—when he had heard the voice of his Beloved just as Francis had heard it on La Verna.

Then he returned to Rome.

During this difficult time, he composed one of his best works

in verse, the *Desconhort,* 69 stanzas of twelve lines each, a cata-
logue of poignant and bitter recollections of the griefs and fail-
ures of years past. This cry of the heart is interesting not only as
a masterpiece of Catalan literature, but also as the story of Raymond's life. He enlists the sympathy of the reader at the outset
by the pathos of the subtitle: "Made by Master Raymond Lull
in his old age, when he saw that neither the pope or the other
lords of the world would put forth a method for the conversion
of the heathen, according as he had prayed them on many and
diverse occasions."

Raymond's serenity appears to have returned once he got the
Desconhort out of his system. He stayed for some time in Rome,
doubtless watching for a favorable opportunity to renew his suit
with Pope Boniface. One evening in the autumn of 1295, he
wandered through a little wood that crowned the Pincian Hill.
The wind drove gusts of amber leaves around him, and his
poetim imagination seized on this to conceive *The Tree of
Science.* The modern edition of this work fills 1,300 large pages.
It was one of the attempts at a complete synthesis of knowledge
which was to make Raymond famous. He used sixteen trees as
symbols, with their branches and leaves representing the various
ramifications of knowledge. The Franciscan Roger Bacon, Raymond's contemporary, was also at work on such a system.

The following year, seeing that he was getting nowhere with
Pope Boniface, Raymond left Rome. After a short stay in Genoa
he came to his well-loved Montpellier, where James of Mallorca
had his residence.

For over eleven years James had fought and schemed to re-
gain his little kingdom—first from his ruthless brother Peter, and
later from Peter's son Alfonso. Popes had intervened often in
the struggle; but their efforts were in vain until, by the treaty of
Anagni, Boniface arranged that James should return to his do-

main, holding it, however, in fief from his nephew.

Raymond hastened to the royal residence, and in the first joy of reunion all sadness and disappointment were forgotten. James still loved his old friend dearly, although his love was now mingled with awe and reverence for Raymond's reputation for sanctity and learning. For Raymond, the King would always be his gentle pupil, noble and just, at odds with an unkind world. The two of them spoke of thwarted ambitions and chilled hopes, and Raymond confessed that he was once more in the grip of an epic depression which seemed to lighten only when he was writing one of his endless streams of books or when he was traveling about on the business of his Beloved.

The King remonstrated with him, saying that it was more fitting to the burden of his years that he seek serenity of mind and spirit. But Raymond replied: "These good things, Jaime, are appealing to your own temperament and will doubtless draw you closer to God if you seek to achieve them. But my own offering must be one of activity. I know that I am mocked—that they call me Raymond the Fantastic and even Raymond the Grasshopper because of my wanderings. I know that my books are looked askance at by many; they say my thoughts are tinged with heresy and my Latin grammar tinged with Catalan! They have called me frenzied and extravagant—yet how can a true lover remain calm when pursuing the Desire of his heart?"

James inclined his head in wry agreement. "I know you too well to dispute the matter. Let us work out our destinies in our own way, then, I in search of peace, you in search of Love."

Soon afterwards Raymond went on to Paris, where he devoted himself in writing and to fruitlessly pleading his case before Philip the Fair. The list of his works produced between 1297 and 1299 suggests the compilation of a committee of experts rather than the efforts of one aging man. He wrote *The Contemplation of Raymond; The Declaration of Raymond,* an attack against Averroism, which was still rife in the schools; and the *Tree of the Philosophy of Love,* presented to the university and to the King and Queen as well. In June of 1299 he wrote one of his finest poems, *The Song of Raymond,* and a book of answers to fifty questions posed by his disciple and friend, Thomas le Myesier, Canon of Arras, who would later become Lull's biographer.

Spent by his literary efforts, he felt a piercing longing for his island home; but even as he wended his way down through France and into Spain he felt tempted to a more active form of apostolate once more. It was the custom of the time to permit debates between Christian preachers and unbelievers in the synagogues and mosques of Spain; so Raymond detoured to Barcelona and remained there for some months trying to convert the Jews of that city.

After this interlude, he moved on to Palma on Mallorca, where he availed himself of the hospitality of the Franciscan friars, taking up his pen once more in the peace of the cloisters. It was there that he composed a poem of six thousand lines, *Medicine for Sin,* which contains a great analysis of prayer; he also wrote numerous lesser works.

He had been in Palma almost a year when the Father Guardian approached him with exciting news. "The latest ship carried a messenger from the East, Master Raymond, with news to lift the heart of a great missionary such as yourself."

Raymond deprecated the praise with a gesture. "Pray tell me what has happened."

"Deliverance so often comes from unexpected places, and it has come to pass that what the crusaders could not do has been accomplished by none other than the Great Tatar himself! He has conquered the Saracens in Syria!"

"Magnificent!" Raymond cried, leaping up from his desk. He began to stride up and down the scriptorium, once more afire with plans. "With so powerful a khan—and one so friendly to Christians—in control of the Holy Land, we shall be able to spread the Faith through Africa and Asia Minor!"

The Father Guardian said, "News reached us that the Khan won a glorious victory over the combined forces of the Sultan of Egypt and the King of Syria, who have now retreated to the sands of Egypt."

"I feel like an old general who hears the far-off sound of trumpets and drummers," Raymond said. "The Holy War is resumed once more, and I must be off to press the advantage while yet I am able."

"You speak like a true warrior bard of the Poverello, Master Raymond. I knew our little place would not hold you when you learned these happy tidings."

"Give me your blessing now, Padre, for I will depart on the winds of dawn." He knelt, and the Father Guardian pronounced the Blessing of St. Francis over the tertiary's snowy head:

"The Lord bless you and keep you.

May he show his face to you

And have mercy on you.

May he turn his countenance toward you

And give you peace."

The next morning, Raymond boarded a ship bound for Cyprus.

Raymond was so impatient to begin his new missionary venture that he rehearsed again and again in his mind his arguments against Islam, recalling especially those he found so effective in Tunis. The great crest of Cyprus loomed up out of the morning mists, and he almost leaped from the boat before it tied up at Famagusta.

Eagerly, he inquired the latest news from Syria, only to reel back in dismay when he heard what had happened. The Khan had been forced to rush back to Persia to quell a rebellion before he had time to consolidate his victory in Syria. The defeated Moslem forces had closed in behind his withdrawal, and the Holy Land was once more lost.

This fresh disappointment was bitter to Raymond, but he had learned to be philosophical at last. Instead of sinking into despondency, he decided to make use of his time on Cyprus by preaching to the local heretics. He approached the ruler of the island for permission, which was granted, and obtained the assistance of a cleric and a servant.

The campaign commenced with Raymond's usual zeal, but inside of a few weeks, the missionary was stricken with a mysterious illness. Physicians diagnosed poisoning, and suspicion centered upon the two associates, who might have been clandestine heretics themselves. The Master of the Temple took Raymond under his protection, bringing him to his house at Limasol and nursing him back to health. During the convalescence, Raymond whiled away the time by writing *The New Rhetoric.*

Prudence dictated that he quit Cyprus; and during the next five years, 1301 through 1305, he traveled about the lands of the Mediterranean, preaching and writing with almost inconceivable vigor. In Armenia he wrote a work on man's duty to God. On a journey home to Mallorca he jotted down a book of a thousand proverbs. In Montpellier, he wrote numerous small works, among them the *Book on Predestination and Free Will,* the *Dispute Between Faith and Understanding,* the *Book on*

Light, the *Book on Law,* the *Book on Memory,* and the *Book of the Ascent and Descent of the Intellect.*

He was now over seventy years old, yet his mind was as keen as it had ever been. He poured out his praise of the Franciscans in one of a hundred sermons written for Sundays and feast-days, part of his *The Great Art of Preaching.* Last and greatest of the books of this period is that with the significant title *Liber de Fine* —*The Book of the End.* By this he is prepared to stand in judgment before the whole court of heaven, even before God himself, on judgment day. He has done all he can; this is the end; and the book reflects a human cry of sheer weariness. It sets out the viewpoints of unbelievers, pagans, heretics, and schismatics, and restates the practical steps for their conversion. It repeats the urgent appeal for the unification of the military orders under one command in a new crusade. Raymond shows himself a most competent military strategist when he discusses the best plans of campaign: the route via Turkey and Armenia is long and difficult; other routes would prove costly or traverse unhealthy regions. The best route is by way of southern Spain, then through Ceuta and Tunis, and he urges the Pope and cardinals to begin at once in God's name. He grieves at the inaction of Christians while the Holy City lies desolate, and prays God to bless this undertaking and bring it to a good and speedy end.

Chapter 8

THE LONG FEUD BETWEEN POPE
Boniface and Philip of France had reached its peak in 1303,
only six years after the Pope had canonized Philip's grandfather,
Louis IX. The scheming monarch insulted Boniface openly and
leveled wild charges of heresy, murder, and invalid election
against him. The temper of the Roman people turned against the
Pontiff, who fled to Anagni. There he was attacked in his palace
by mercenaries led by one of the powerful Colonna family,
thrown into a cell, and finally rescued by the local people. Another group of intriguers, the Orsini, took him back to Rome as
their prisoner. He died on October 11, 1303, as a result of the
ill treatment he had received.

Pope Boniface was succeeded by the peacemaking Dominican,
Benedict XI, who sought to restore relations with Philip. But the
king would not be content with mere treaties of amity; he insisted that a General Council be called to condemn the alleged
perfidies of Boniface. Benedict refused to do this, and within a
short time he was dead. Sinister rumors of poison were circulated, and the cardinals convened at Perugia amid the undis-
guised menacings of Philip.

It took eleven months to elect the next pope, and few people were surprised that the choice should fall upon a Frenchman. He was Raymond Bertrand de Goth, Archbishop of Bordeaux and lifelong friend of Philip. Unsavory though the politics of the election may have seemed, they portended well for Raymond and his plans.

The new Pope paused at Montpellier on his way to Lyons, where he had chosen to be crowned. He received James of Mallorca, James of Aragon, and Raymond himself, who recounts that the conversation turned to the hopes for a new crusade. When James of Aragon had pledged his loyalty and aid, he presented a copy of Raymond's *Liber de Fine* to the Pontiff. After the coronation in November, 1305, there would be days of quiet when the Pope might study Raymond's proposals.

Weeks passed, and Pope Clement V failed to summon the old missionary. Tales circulated concerning Philip's incessant demands for revenge upon the memory of Boniface, and he was also pressing the Pope to dissolve the powerful Order of the Knights Templars so that he might confiscate its wealth. Raymond used every influence he could think of to hasten the decision of the Holy See concerning his new crusade; but the answer was always the same; it would be taken under advisement.

Matters had to be left at this temporary impasse. Raymond went to Paris in the spring, hoping to bury his disappointment in teaching and writing at the university.

One morning, on his way to the Sorbonne, he was greeted by a young Franciscan scholar.

"Good morning to you, my son," Raymond replied. "Your accent tells me that you are English."

"From Oxford, Master Raymond. I follow the lectures of my famous fellow-Franciscan Master John Duns, called the Scot. I am on my way to his lecture now. One must be very early to be sure of getting a good place."

Raymond smiled. "Then we must walk together, for we have the same goal. It has been my desire to hear this excellent young man. His reputation has traveled far abroad, even though he only received his Master's diploma last year."

"When he lectures, the other halls are empty!" exclaimed the young friar. "Today he speaks on a topic which should appeal to you—the *rationes seminales* of St. Augustine. What a memorable morning this will be with two such great Masters in the same hall!"

The place was very crowded when they arrived. Every seat was taken, and the overflow of the crowd filled every corner of the room. Raymond and his young companion finally found a place at the edge of the rostrum itself. Punctually at seven the slight figure of Master John appeared. Raymond noted him well as he approached the cathedra—an erect head, deepset eyes that seemed to hold blue fire in their depths, a difinied yet unassuming air.

He began to speak, and his rich accent seemed to add resonance to the Latin. The strong burr had all the freshness of heather-sweet hills and the simplicity of the Franciscan vision of all things. The students sat motionless, following the brilliant metaphysical arguments that were at once complex and lucid.

At the close of the lecture, Raymond pressed close to offer his congratulations; then with characteristic impulsiveness asked if he might address the students. Duns Scotus graciously acceded and listened attentively himself while Raymond delivered a brilliant *ex tempore* lecture on the Divine Nature. When he had concluded, the young Franciscan *Doctor Subtilis* linked his arm in that of the old tertiary *Doctor Illuminatus,* and together they left the Sorbonne and walked in earnest conversation along the banks of the Seine in the May sunshine.

Raymond wrote several works during his stay in Paris. Among them was a petition addressed to the professors of the university, asking them to draw up a set of arguments suitable for the conversion of unbelievers. He offered a list already compiled by himself, and stated that he was about to return to Africa and preach to the Moors.

He went from Paris to Mallorca, and from there sailed to the beautiful town of Bougie, 120 miles east of Algiers, which he had chosen as the scene of his renewed crusade.

His timing of the mission was as unhappy as had been his importuning of Philip and Pope Clement. He could scarcely have chosen a worse time for his entry. Tunis and Bougie were at war; and, even more disastrous for Raymond, a religious fanatic had for some time been tactlessly harrassing the people of the town, whose tempers were now frayed to the snapping point.

Raymond had decided to speak in the bazaar, seeking an opportunity to expound simplified doctrines he thought would reach the common people. He spoke with fire and enthusiasm, hardly noticing that the faces of the crowd were ugly and unsympathetic. An insult rang out—then another, and within minutes the marketplace was a howling mob. Raymond was hauled off to appear before the kadi, the chief judge of the city. The death penalty seemed assured, but Raymond's calm demeanor and obvious erudition so impressed the kadi that he ruled that Raymond should be put into prison.

The bloodthirsty mob yelled in fury when the decision was announced, demanding that Raymond should be thrown to them so that they could stone him to death. But the kadi held firm, either because he wished to be able to hold further discussion with Raymond, or because he wanted to see him formally tried and condemned by the council.

So Great a Lover

When at length Raymond was thrown into a foul dark cell, he consoled himself that he was once more actively pursuing his Lord, counting all his afflictions as blessings since they were endured for the sake of Love.

At that time Bougie was one of the most important trading centers on the coast of North Africa; and Italian merchants had great storehouses, churches, and even houses and baths there. They were treated with respect by the Moors. When some Genoese merchants heard of Raymond's imprisonment, they asked at once that he be given better lodging and kinder treatment. Unexpectedly, their request was granted.

Courtesy and cruelty lay side by side in the Moorish character. It was without any feeling of inconsistency that Raymond's jailers moved him from the fetid den where he had been flung to die to a comfortable place of detention where he was treated almost with deference. Some of the most learned men of the city came to visit him, and they continued on a higher plane the discussions which had originally caused all of Raymond's sufferings.

He was delighted at the opportunity to debate with the Moslems once more. They on their part felt that Raymond would be a most valuable convert to Islam, and offered him riches, honors and women if he would but renounce Christ. He turned their blandishments against them, saying that they had but short-lived and sensual pleasures to offer him, whereas, if they would but hear him, he could assure them of life everlasting and an imperishable treasure of heavenly joy.

One Moor, named Hamar, held such lengthy and detailed discussions with him that the two of them decided to write up the debates in the form of a book. Entitled *The Disputation of Raymond the Christian and Hamar the Saracen,* it was written in Arabic with the intention of presenting it to the kadi. But it fell instead into the hands of the king of Bougie, who ordered Raymond to be expelled from the city forthwith, and put to death if he returned. There could have been no more sincere tribute paid to Raymond's apologetics.

The old man was bundled into a boat bound for Genoa. He was seventy-five years old, but his mind still blazed with plans for continuing the work he had begun anew.

As the ship drew near the Italian coast, a storm sprang up with unexpected violence. There were shouts from the sailors, who scrambled frantically to furl the sails and make fast the bales of merchandise that were skidding dangerously about the deck. Panic began to sweep through the ship as the wind grew stronger, carrying away most of the rigging. Men shrieked and wept with fear; a few, like Raymond, threw themselves onto the wet and reeling deck and prayed.

With the southwest wind howling behind them, they tried to make for the shelter of the river Arno and Pisa. But just as they managed to turn their crippled craft toward land they were hit broadside by a gigantic wave. In seconds, the ship capsized and sank, carrying most of her passengers and crew with her. A few survivors, including the venerable preacher, managed to cling to a spar and were eventually saved by a rescue vessel from Pisa.

As the castaways were carried ashore, the storm faded away as quickly as it had sprung up, leaving a bright and tossing sea that seemed innocent of any ability to harm men.

All Pisa rang with the fame of the splendid old man who had barely escaped with his life from the hands of the Moors and from the anger of the sea. Raymond was received as one marked for a great destiny. When he found that the people were so generously in sympathy with him, he proposed to the city commune the founding of a new military order and the organizing of a new and powerful crusade. The Pisans responded enthusiastically, not only with generous financial aid, but also with letters to the

Pope, pledging their support for the new venture.

Raymond's journey to Genoa was a trimphal procession, and in that city he was greeted as a hero. Noble ladies and devout widows poured their jewels into his hands. The entire city rallied to his cause, and he left Genoa with over thirty thousand florins to be used to advance the crusade.

He set sail for France, knowing that this time the Pope would be unable to put him off. As the ship pulled away from the dock the cry, "God wills it! God wills it!" floated from the crowd that had gathered to see him embark. It was the rallying cry of the crusades.

"God wills it, may his will be done," responded the old man.

The singing sailors spread sail, and the captain came and stood beside Raymond. "The time will come soon when these waters will swarm with a magnificent Christian fleet, Master Raymond."

"God grant that these old eyes will be spared to witness it."

"Amen to that, Master. As for me, I'll welcome the chance to settle some old scores against those pirate dogs. Only last winter two of their accursed corsairs bore down on us, galleys of forty oars each. They drew little water and made great speed. Luckily for us, the wind was in our favor and we ran ahead of them. But they closed in near enough to pour a rain of javelins and stones on us, and near enough, too, for us to see that the galleys were rowed by poor shackled Christians. Just as the two corsairs converged upon us, we tacked suddenly. They collided with each other while we made good our escape."

"Bravo, Captain!"

"The sight of those poor wretches chained to the oars haunts me still. It made me swear a solemn oath to sink a score of Moorish galleys before I die. We are far stronger on the sea than on land, Master Raymond. Why do we not muster our whole sea strength against the infidel pigs?"

91

"I have had precisely this plan in mind, and I intend to propose it to His Holiness. Listen! We will begin the Holy War at sea. Superior numbers and brave, experienced men such as yourself will bring us quick victory. Then we will send our armies through Constantinople, take Syria, and move into Egypt. A second army starting from Granada and advancing from Spain into Tunis will link up with the first, free Africa, and subdue the infidel forever."

The captain's look showed his admiration. "You should have been a general, Master! What a splendid plan for conquest!"

Raymond's gaze clouded at the words of approval. He remembered the scorn he had held for the men of the sword, his confidence that victory over the Moslems could be won by weapons of the mind alone. Perhaps it could—but the wisdom of his old age showed him that such a course would require centuries of patient effort, the persistent work of thousands of missionaries. And he was one man, and he was old. . . .

He left the ship at Aiguesmortes and went to stay for a time in Montpellier, that haven where he could rest and prepare himself. He wrote the *Book on the Acquisition of the Holy Land,* addressed to the Pope, then set out to plead his cause in person once more.

Chapter 9

In March 1309, Pope Clement V permanently settled his court at a Dominican monastery in Avignon, not far from Montpellier. Raymond was received there by the ailing Pontiff and poured out the generous subscriptions of the Pisans and Genoese, together with warm accounts of the people's enthusiasm towards the new crusade.

"We have read your book, Raymond our son," Clement said, "and we find your plan a good one. We shall put preparations for the new crusade into the hands of the Hospitallers and Templars, and we ourselves will pledge ninety thousand florins from the papal treasury."

The old man's eyes filled with tears of joy. "Your Holiness," he began brokenly, "if you knew what your words meant to me—"

"The Holy War is but one phase of the conquest of the infidel, Raymond. We charge you now to commit to writing those things which will aid our cause with the kings and princes. They oppress me sorely, as you know, with their demands for vengeance upon one another and upon the memory of our unfortunate predecessor upon the throne of Peter."

"I will do as you command, Holy Father."

"Next year, if all goes well, a General Council will be convened at Vienne. You must be prepared to put forth concrete plans of action at that time."

Raymond pledged that he would be ready. Then, leaving Avignon, he went to Paris. Sad news awaited him there. Five months before, the great John Duns Scotus had passed to his eternal reward. He was only 43 years old.

The scholars and masters of the university clamored for Raymond to lecture to them, and his discourses on theology, philosophy, and the natural sciences soon became famous. A deputation from the university did him the signal honor of coming to the house where he stayed to present him with a parchment of praise for his work. He later received a second diploma of commendation when his works were examined at the request of King Philip. Unscrupulous though this monarch was in his politics, he had great admiration and respect for Raymond and gave him a letter of recommendation for use in his travels.

During a previous stay in Paris, Raymond had fired his first shot into the ranks of the Averroists. Now, as though he knew this was to be his last opportunity, he gathered all the energies of his mind for a final offensive. He had studied the tactics used by the Franciscan St. Bonaventure, and now poured out his condemnation, not of Averroes himself, who was an infidel and knew no better, but of those Christians who adopted and spread his teachings.

Scores of books and pamphlets flowed from his pen, including *The Dispute of Raymond and an Averroist, The Book of Contradiction between Raymond and an Averroist, Discourses Against the Errors of Averroism,* and many others. In another work, *Concerning a Question Very Exalted and Deep,* Raymond tells of a dispute between a Saracen and a Christian on their respective faiths. It is likely that this was written from the memory of an actual dispute between Raymond and an Arab, and the author is struck by the irony of a situation where he is about to travel to the land of the infidels to convert them, while the unbeliever has brought his doctrine right to the intellectual center of Christendom.

Among the writings he prepared for the Council of Vienne was *Petition to the General Council.* It recommended that Averroism be finally condemned; that the loose legal system, so open to abuse and corruption, be tightened up on the model of his own *Art of Law;* that the science of medicine should be freed from the shackles of tradition in favor of the method advocated by his fellow Franciscan, Roger Bacon—namely, observation and experiment; that luxury and multiple offices should be forbidden the clergy, who should adopt a plain decorous dress, distinct from that of laymen. He further petitioned that his request of more than 30 years, the foundation of missionary colleges, should be granted. Finally, he sought the unification of the military Orders and the setting aside of a tithe from all secular princes for the new crusade.

The Council of Vienne was postponed for a year, owing to delay in the investigations against the Knights Templars, whom Philip of France sought to suppress. Raymond impatiently wrote an urgent letter in verse to all the prelates who were to take part in the Council, urging quick and zealous action. The spirited tone of the verses reminds us that medieval Europe had an intimate family atmosphere, where a man such as Raymond could affectionately admonish or rebuke cardinals and princes, since they were all brothers in the family of Christ.

In 1311, he set out for Vienne, and while he was traveling news reached him of the death of James II of Mallorca. For 65 years their lives had advanced together, so that it seemed to the lonely old man that it was a part of himself that had perished.

He remained in Vienne all through the eight months of the Council. One of the books he composed, *Phantasticus, or The Dispute Between a Cleric and Raymond the Fantastic,* shows all too clearly the repute he enjoyed in certain Church circles.

But whether or not his personality was grounds for amusement, his proposals were held in utter seriousness. The Council decreed that colleges for the study of oriental languages should be established at Rome, Paris, Oxford, Salamanca, and Bologna. It ordered that plans for a crusade should be drawn up. The Templars having been suppressed to the satisfaction of Philip, the Council decreed that the property of the Order be taken over by the Knights of St. John for the promulgation of the Holy War. King Philip promised his full support and that of his nobles, and a Church levy of a tithe was ordered for the next six years. Finally, many of Raymond's wise suggestions for ecclesiastical reform were put to the bishops attending the Council for their written proposals and recommendations, and rules were laid down that were later to be acted upon by Pope John XXII after Raymond's death.

Raymond knew that he did not have much more time. Now in his eightieth year, he began to prepare for the coming of Sister Death. He drew up his will in April, 1313. Worldly goods he had none, and he was indifferent to the fate of his body; but his instructions concerning his beloved books were precise.

When his affairs were in order, he determined to use every moment of life that remained to him in working for his Beloved. In May, 1313, he went to Sicily. With the approval of King Francis and the Archbishop, he drew up plans for the conversion of the Jews and Saracens of the island, also preparing a great number of pamphlets on problems which might prove stumbling-blocks to converts.

So Great a Lover

In his eleventh hour, he determined to return once more to Africa. But first, he would return to take his last leave of his island home. He reached Mallorca in May, 1314, and spent the summer there in a final pilgrimage of love among the familiar places. He prostrated himself among the crags of Mount Randa, his mountain of vision; he mourned at Miramar, from whence his first college had been long since expelled; he knelt beside the tomb of James in the cathedral, praying a place of "refreshment, light and peace" for the soul of his old friend.

Then on an August morning he took ship for Bougie. He had asked for letters of safe conduct from King James of Aragon to be sent to the King of Tunis; and after a short stay in Bougie, he went on to Tunis, confident of a friendly welcome.

The period spent in that city, during the last year of his life, was one of the happiest and most successful in Raymond's career. A number of the wisest scholars were converted to Christianity. Raymond wrote to James of Aragon, requesting that he send a former pupil of his, the brilliant Franciscan Fray Simon de Puigcerda, to translate his recent writings, the fruit of his discussions with the Moors, into Latin.

When he was sure that matters in Tunis were in good hands, he moved off once more to Bougie, arriving late in 1315. This time he did not wait to address the scholars and wise men. Instead, either forgetting what had happened to him in past years when he had dared address the ignorant, or else proceeding in the face of the inevitable consequences, he once again set about to preach in the bazaar.

Deliberately, he ascended the stairs of a convenient mosque, turned with arms flung wide, and called on the crowd to listen to his words and come to Christ. The wrath of the Moslems burst like a sundered dam, and he was borne down under a flood of blows and stones. Within a few moments, the body of Raymond Lull lay at the foot of the stairs in a pool of blood. The mob slunk away, and news of the affair spread rapidly.

Luigi de Pastorga and Stefano Colombo, the two merchants who had met Raymond on his maiden voyage to the African mission field, learned of his fate and hastened to inquire what had been done with his body. To their horror, they learned that it still lay where it had fallen. They went at once with two servants and a litter, finding their old friend toward the end of the afternoon.

The Franciscan habit was stiff with blackened blood, and a horde of flies clouded around the still form. "Alas, poor old Navigator," Stefano Colombo cried, "that your voyagings for Christ should reap a death so wretched!"

One of Raymond's eyes opened, and the merchants gasped in amazement. "There was another Death far worse than mine," came a cracked whisper.

"Alive, by the Virgin!" said Colombo. "Luigi! Mario! Help me lift him to the litter!"

Raymond was indeed alive, but his injuries were clearly mortal. The Genoese hastened with him to their ship and set sail at once. They had expected him to expire at any moment, but miraculously, he clung to life. They were but a day out to sea when the wind veered and the ship was carried swiftly westward, instead of north towards Genoa. The very winds of heaven were bearing Raymond irresistibly toward the islands of his birth.

The days went by, and one evening the lookout sighted an island. Mallorca loomed in the scarlet of the sunset. Stefano Colombo carried the wracked body of Raymond to the deck.

'Bring me forward, dear friend," the old man whispered. "For just as Francis asked to be carried to Assisi when he felt the approach of Sister Death, so do I long to see my dear Isle of Love."

So Great a Lover

The dying man raised a thin, trembling arm and pointed over the vivid waters. Colombo bent close to hear his last words. "Far, far beyond Mallorca and Spain lies another great land more vast than Africa. In times to come, millions of men will praise God there. It will more than compensate for all we have lost in Africa."

The tired hand dropped, and the weary head fell back on the broad chest of Colombo, whose children's children would retell these last words of a great man until finally one of them, Christoforo, would put the prophecy to the test.

Around Raymond were the sounds he knew so well—the creaking spars and rigging, the slap of waves against the ship's side, the song of seamen going about their work. His life's pursuit had finally come to an end. He breathed, *"In manus tuas, Domine, commendo spiritum meam,"* and gave himself at last into the hands of his Beloved.

Epilogue

"ONE BORN OUT OF DUE TIME"—
so the Apostle of the Gentiles describes himself. How aptly
Blessed Raymond Lull could have used that phrase in describing himself. The times in which he lived were tragically out of
joint for the great missionary-mystic; and although he was one
of the most versatile of the manysided geniuses of his age, his
voice went largely unheeded amid the tumult of warring kings.

The times were also unpropitious in that the 13th century saw
many popes of brief and troubled reign. Blessed Raymond lived
through the pontificates of no fewer than eighteen of Peter's
successors, and died as the papacy declined towards the so-
called Babylonian Captivity at Avignon.

The very year after his death, John XXII founded chairs of
Hebrew, Arabic, and Chaldean in the universities of Paris, Oxford, Salamanca, and Bologna—just as Raymond had proposed
in his *Petition*. From the time of Pope John XXII onwards,
many of Raymond's reforms were gradually introduced. A small
crusade was eventually launched, winning several victories before enthusiasm waned.

In 1512 the Fifth Lateran Council adopted Blessed Raymond's methods of combatting heresy. His proposal to break the

power of the Saracens on the sea was put into effect at the battle of Lepanto in 1571, when the combined fleets of Genoa, Spain, Venice, Naples, and Sicily gained a decisive victory over the Turks. Three centuries after his death his program of missionary organization and method were adopted by the Sacred Congregation of the Propaganda.

It was partly due to Raymond's active apostolate among the Moslems and his keen observation on their psychology and traditions that the Franciscans secured the guardianship of the Holy Places. A few years before Raymond's death, Bibias II, Caliph of Egypt, granted exclusive rights to the Franciscans to live in Jerusalem, at the Holy Sepulchre, and at Bethlehem. In spite of occasional persecutions and martyrdom, the friars remain guardians of the Holy Places to this day.

The great achievement of Blessed Raymond on the purely secular level was to do for his native Catalan dialect what Dante did for his own Tuscan language: create in it such living and lasting literature as to raise it above other dialects in subtlety and strength. He made Catalan worthy of being used along with Latin as a vehicle of philosophic thought. He is regarded as the herald of Catalan poetry, not only in his many verse compositions, but also—and often more so—in his fine lyrical prose.

It is true that many foolish and extravagant claims were made for him by admirers more loving than learned, especially in the centuries immediately after his death. He was credited by some with having written 5,000 works. We can make for him the far prouder claim that, of 243 authenticated works, several have stood the test of more than six centuries and are still enjoyably readable today. He was alleged to be an expert on everything from mathematics to music, from astronomy to alchemy. Here again we can say that though his amazing mind did range up and down the vast scale of the sciences, he never lost balance nor forgot that all knowledge and all science and art are but steps in the journey of the mind to God.

Even though Blessed Raymond's writings were examined by many competent and critical experts during his lifetime and highly praised for their orthodoxy, they became the object of bitter censure from some small-minded critics after his death. The *Doctor Illuminatus* had been dead only fifty years when the Dominican Inquisitor, Nicholas Eymeric, chaplain to Pope Gregory XI, directed a torrent of condemnation against Raymond's spiritual status and character, describing him as a fantastic, a heretic, an ignoramus, and perhaps even a tool of the Evil One. Eymeric produced a hundred propositions from Raymond's writings which, lifted out of context, he showed to be heretical. He claimed to have a bull of condemnation from Pope Gregory in 1376. But Eymeric was finally and shamefully confounded when, in 1419, the condemnatory bull was officially declared spurious, and it was found that some of the hundred condemned propositions were not taken from the works of Raymond Lull at all.

Raymond's cult flourished throughout the 15th and 16th centuries. Chairs of Lullian science were founded in the schools at Randa and in the University of Palma, as well as in many universities and colleges on the mainland. The commentaries on his work far exceeded his own literary output, prodigious as that was.

Tradition holds, although no written proof remains, that Raymond was beatified by Pope Leo X early in the 16th century. Despite the fact that, between 1772 and 1777, the Dominican bishop of Mallorca made determined efforts to root out the very name of Raymond Lull from the memory of the islanders, seizing all portraits and documents relating to him, removing his feast from the *Ordo,* and forbidding the name Raymond to be given in baptism, Raymond Lull was formally beatified by Pope Pius IX in 1847.

Today his enemies are in oblivion, but Blessed Raymond enjoys an ever-growing popularity. In his native Palma the Casa Oleo houses a Lullian academy, while his memory is preserved on Mount Randa by the Franciscan community there. His feast is kept by the Franciscans, with that of two other missionary martyrs of the First Order, on September 5; the Conventuals observe his feast on July 4, and the Third Order Regular on July 3. The magnificent tomb of Blessed Raymond can be seen in the Franciscan church in Palma. A masterpiece of delicately carved Gothic design, it lies in the second chapel at the chancel end of the church, on the epistle side of the high altar. There are seven niches supported by brackets, representing the arts and sciences in which he excelled: Geometry, Arithmetic, Logic, Grammar, Medicine, Rhetoric, and Astronomy. A recumbent statue of the *Beatus* lies on an alabaster sarcophagus, and on his resting place is engraved an apt phrase from one of his books:

HERE LIES A LOVER
WHO HAS DIED FOR HIS BELOVED AND FOR LOVE